JACOPO

BERENGARIO

DA CARPI

A

SHORT

INTRODUCTION

TO

ANATOMY

(ISAGOGAE BREVES)

JACOPO BERENGARIO DA CARPI

A SHORT
INTRODUCTION
TO
ANATOMY

(ISAGOGAE BREVES)

Translated with an Introduction and
Historical Notes by

L. R. LIND

and with Anatomical Notes by PAUL G. ROOFE

THE UNIVERSITY OF CHICAGO PRESS

THE UNIVERSITY OF CHICAGO COMMITTEE
ON PUBLICATIONS IN BIOLOGY AND MEDICINE

EMMET B. BAY · LOWELL T. COGGESHALL
PETER P. H. DE BRUYN · LESTER R. DRAGSTEDT
THOMAS PARK · WILLIAM H. TALIAFERRO

Library of Congress Catalog Number: 59-10426

THE UNIVERSITY OF CHICAGO PRESS, CHICAGO 37
Cambridge University Press, London, N.W. 1, England
The University of Toronto Press, Toronto 5, Canada

© 1959 by The University of Chicago. Published 1959. Composed and printed by THE UNIVERSITY OF CHICAGO PRESS, Chicago, Illinois, U.S.A.

TO

THE AMERICAN

ASSOCIATION

OF

ANATOMISTS

&

PARTICULARLY

TO

H. W. MAGOUN

ACKNOWLEDGMENTS

Th is translation of the *Isagogae breves,* or *Short Introduction to Anatomy,* by Berengario da Carpi (*ca.* 1460–1530) was suggested to me by Dr. Horace W. Magoun, of the Department of Anatomy at the University of California, Los Angeles. His genial persuasion was expressed in the following words: "This translation would fill a most valuable transition between Charles Singer's translation of Mundinus' *Anatomy,* representing the medieval period, and your own translation of the *Epitome* of Vesalius, representing the High Renaissance." Dr. Magoun, with courteous patience and helpfulness, has furthered the progress of the translation by arranging for my use of the 1535 edition through Dr. Robert J. Moes of Los Angeles, who generously lent me the copy from his fine collection of books on the history of medicine. To Dr. Magoun and to Dr. Moes, I offer thanks for their assistance, especially for photostats used in making the illustrations.

I am grateful to my good friend and colleague Dr. Paul G. Roofe, chairman of the Department of Anatomy, University of Kansas, for the Anatomical Notes he has contributed to the book; they will enable the reader to follow more readily the descriptions of Berengario. Dr. Roofe also made the preliminary photographs of the illustrations.

The Library of the History of Medicine at the University of Kansas School of Medicine, famous for its collection of rare books, enabled me to use the 1523 edition and to collate it throughout with the 1535 edition, the last to be printed. I am indebted to the careful co-operation of G. S. T. Cavanagh, Librarian at the University of Kansas Medical Center, who not only supplied me with a photostat of the 1523 edition but brought to my notice two useful references to Berengario in recent literature, placing at my disposal the resources of the Library. I am also grateful to Miss Phoebe Peck, of the Library, for her competent help in haunts familiar to me from earlier association with the late Dr. Logan Clendening. Miss Madeline Stanton, of the Historical Library, Yale Medical Library, kindly made it possible for me to collate the first (1522) edition by interlibrary loan.

I wish to record here a special debt of gratitude to Signor Vittorio Putti, without whose admirable book, *Berengario da Carpi: Saggio biografico e bibliografico seguito dalla traduzione del "De fractura calvae sive cranei"* (Bologna: L. Cappelli, 1937), I could not have written my introduction. The thorough, scholarly method of this book and its assemblage of valuable material place all Berengarian scholars under a deep obligation to its author.

ACKNOWLEDGMENTS

Dr. Ralph Major, professor emeritus in the University of Kansas School of Medicine, has read the manuscript and made several suggestions for which I thank him. I am deeply grateful, finally, to Dr. Loren C. MacKinney, professor of medieval history at the University of North Carolina, for his very careful comments and corrections; his knowledge of the period in which Berengario wrote and his understanding of medieval medicine have saved me from error more than once. None of those to whom I express my appreciation for assistance so generously given shares in the results of my own oversight, wherever these may be found.

L. R. LIND

CONTENTS

LIST OF ILLUSTRATIONS

INTRODUCTION

INTRODUCTION

THE LIFE AND WORKS OF
JACOPO BERENGARIO DA CARPI

Many of the most brilliant achievements of Renaissance medicine were accomplished by Italians; in fact, one might say that, for much of the Middle Ages and the Renaissance, medicine was pre-eminently an Italian science. Among the most important Italian anatomists of the early period was Berengario da Carpi or, as he is variously known, Jacopo Berengario, Jacopo da Carpi, and simply Carpi, from the little town between Mantua and Modena where he was born. It was Paolo Guaitoli who discovered that Berengario had all his life concealed his true name, Barigazzi: only in his last will did he reveal himself as *Iacopus filius quondam Magistri Faustini de Barigatiis*.

Whence, then, Berengario? The name does not appear on the title pages of his books published during his lifetime. It is found only at the beginning of the dedicatory letter to Alberto Pio in the *Isagogae breves* and in the subscription. Signor Vittorio Putti conjectured that the name Berengario arose from one of the many corruptions of Barigazzi which appear in a number of notarial documents preserved in the Archivio Notarile of Carpi and in the Guaitoli archives. Berengario himself always preferred the simple name Carpus or De Carpo, which he places at the head of all his books. Under the circumstances, Da Carpi (on the analogy of Da Vinci) is the simplest and most reasonable form. But since Berengario da Carpi is the appellation by which for centuries he has been known and by which he is called in all scientific manuals and histories of medicine, it seems wise to follow established practice in this book as well.

Berengario's father, Faustino, was a barber-surgeon from whom the son learned anatomy and whom he assisted in dissections. Berengario was one of five children, two boys and three girls. The date of his birth is unknown but must fall around 1460. His father was a respectable practitioner; he attended fairly prominent patients and healed them successfully. His feats in operating on the diseased uterus are described in the *Isagogae breves* (1522) and in the *Commentary on the Anatomy of Mundinus* (1521), folio 225; the feat described in the latter book was accomplished around 1490, when Berengario, already a graduate of Bologna, assisted his father.

In *De fractura cranei* (1518), folio 33b, Berengario tells how, while still *satis juvenis,* he operated on three serious cranial fractures. He believed firmly in early application to one's profession and drew most of his knowledge from practical experience. He mentions no medical teacher other than his father in his books and seems never to have studied in any medical school before he went to Bologna for his doctorate.

He spent his youth at Carpi with his family and in the service and company of Alberto Pio, son of Lionello Pio, Lord of Carpi. The great Aldus Manutius, the Humanist printer, was the teacher of both Alberto Pio and Berengario at Carpi. Alberto was perhaps fifteen years younger than Berengario, and it is not to be supposed that their friendship, hinted at in the dedicatory letter to the *Isagogae,* could have been intimate. Neither Aldus nor Alberto mentions Berengario in writing, although he became famous in their lifetimes. Berengario's Latin style does not lead us to believe that he was the best of students of composition, but it was always his pleasure to claim acquaintance with famous Humanists and philosophers. Manutius lived and taught at Carpi from 1469 to 1477; long after his departure Berengario obtained his degree at Bologna, August 4, 1489.

Throughout these years Carpi was beset with troubles. Giberto Pio, son of Marco Pio, uncle of Alberto, schemed for years to rob his cousins of their rights. The factions which thus arose sought assistance from Pope, Emperor, or whatever prince cared to embroil himself in their quarrel. At last Ercole I, Duke of Ferrara, invested with authority as a peacemaker by the Emperor Maximilian but playing his own astute game as well, forced both parties at Carpi to give up their possessions to him. Actually he acquired only the holdings of Giberto, who retired to Bologna and received in exchange the fief of Sassuolo on July 16, 1499. Berengario demonstrated his loyalty to the house of Pio when he spoke openly and insultingly against the Duke of Ferrara, according to the testimony of Tommaso della Volta. On October 17, 1500, he was condemned for his bold words to pay a fine of one hundred ducats or have his nose cut off. Berengario's father paid the fine and thus preserved his son's nose, but Berengario found it wise to leave Carpi.

In the preface to his *Commentary on the Anatomy of Mundinus* Berengario calls Bologna *mea altrice,* the nurse of his learning. The certificate of approval for his degree as *magister* exists in the Archbishop's Archives at Bologna. Although the study of medicine there had declined toward the end of the fifteenth century, the renown of Bologna still attracted students from all of Europe. Moreover, it was no doubt a relief for Berengario to escape at Bologna the political influence of Duke Ercole of Ferrara.

Among his teachers and colleagues at Bologna were Hieronymo Manfredi, Leonello dei Vittori da Faenza, Gabriele Zerbi, and Alessandro Achillini. Manfredi wrote a small popular anatomy, published by Charles Singer in

Studies in the History and Method of Science, Volume I (Oxford University Press, 1917): The *Anothomia* of Hieronymo Manfredi, transcribed and translated by A. Mildred Westland, and described by Singer as a study in early Renaissance anatomy. Leonello dei Vittori was a pioneer in distinguishing children's diseases from those of adults. That Berengario studied under Zerbi is probable from frequent mention of him in Berengario's works and from the keen polemic which he directs against Zerbi in his *Commentary on Mundinus* (fol. 17b). Berengario continued to hate Zerbi even after the latter's death in 1505; he also took delight in the execution of Zerbi's sons, hanged as thieves under Pope Julius at Rome. With Achillini he was on terms of mutual respect; perhaps he worked with him in the dissecting room. Berengario's tendency toward malice revealed itself in his remark on Achillini's *In Mundini anatomiam annotationes* (Bologna, 1524); this he called "confusa Anatomia."

We know little of the years in Berengario's life during which, after the granting of his degree in 1489, he was making his reputation. The troubled history of Carpi during the last decade of the fifteenth century seems to have provided Berengario with an exciting environment and, practically speaking, plenty of dead and wounded bodies on which to practice anatomy. The outbreak of syphilis in Italy after the victory of King Charles VIII of France at Fornovo in 1495 gave Berengario another fruitful field of opportunity but one in which his fame became somewhat tarnished. Berengario treated syphilis with mercury, often vainly as far as his patients' recovery was concerned but with great profit to himself. Benvenuto Cellini (*Autobiography* [Everyman ed., 1907], pp. 51–53) describes his meeting with Berengario in the following words:

There came to Rome [in 1526] a very great surgeon called Maestro Giacomo da Carpi. This clever man, in the course of his other professional duties, took certain desperate cases of the French evil. Now in Rome priests are particularly liable to this disease, especially the richest of them. Well, when this distinguished man became known, he declared he would cure the malady in the most marvellous fashion by means of fumigations. But before beginning a cure he first bargained for his fees, and it was by hundreds and not by tens of crowns that these were reckoned. . . . He was learned and could speak admirably on the subject of medicine. The Pope wished him to remain in his service; but Carpi said he would not be in the service of any one in the world, and whoever wanted him might come and seek him. A very shrewd person he was, too, and he did wisely in leaving Rome; for not many months after, all those whom he had treated were a hundred times worse than before; and he would have been killed had he stopped.

Later, writing to Messer Alberto (*ibid.,* p. 291), Benvenuto recalled:

This is copied from a silver jug of such and such a weight, which I made at such and such a time for that quack Jacopo, the Carpi surgeon. He came to Rome, and stayed there six months, daubing with his unguents scores of lords and unlucky gentlemen, whom he fleeced of many thousand ducats. At that time I made this vase for him, and another different one; and he paid me wretchedly for my pains. And now all those poor wretches in Rome, whom he daubed, are crippled today, and in very bad case.

The *profumi* and *unguenti* of which Cellini speaks were, of course, guaiac (see **R. S.** Munger in the *Journal of the History of Medicine,* IV [1949], 196–229) and mercury.

In 1502 Berengario was named a master of studies at Bologna, specifically Lecturer in Surgery, a post dependent upon political favor and difficult for a stranger in Bologna to attain; it was a position equivalent perhaps to our own Distinguished Service professorships. This triumph was made all the more remarkable by the fact that the Bentivoglio family, which controlled Bologna, was hostile to the party of Alberto Pio. Berengario of course does not seem to have had any share of this hostility; yet, had he become an adherent of the Bentivoglio in the early sixteenth century—so intricate were such relationships in Italy during the Renaissance—he might not later have been able to avail himself of the patronage of Pope Julius II, enemy of the Bentivoglio. At any rate, Berengario's gifts for diplomacy must have been great.

He probably owed his medical success not to his fame as a theorist in anatomy (he had not as yet published any books) but to his skill in surgery and practical medicine. His stipend of 100 lire annually at Bologna began on May 5, 1503. There is no evidence that he ever taught at Pavia, as has been often asserted.

By 1506, the date when he received Bolognese citizenship from Julius II upon the Pope's triumphal entry into Bologna, Berengario had married; shortly thereafter a daughter, Faustina, was born to him. She died, however, before the date of his last will (1528). In 1507 he inherited by the death of his father the property of his paternal aunt.

In 1508 the plague broke out in Bologna. Severe sanitary measures were taken by the city authorities, and Berengario was appointed to the position of what would today be called city commissioner of health, in charge of fighting the plague. He held this appointment in addition to his university post until 1512. In 1513 Pope Leo X ordered the Senate of Bologna to allow Berengario to go to Florence to attend Alessandro Soderini, a relative of the Pope, in his illness. To Giulio de' Medici (Pope Clement VII) Berengario dedicated his *Commentary on the Anatomy of Mundinus;* to Lorenzo de' Medici, Duke of Urbino, he dedicated his *Tractatus de fractura cranei.* He led a vigorous public life at Bologna in addition to his scholarly activities, although he did not begin to write his books until he was past fifty.

There are episodes in the life of Berengario which cast ugly shadows upon his otherwise well-earned fame and standing in Bologna. History shows him to have been rapacious, greedy, and ruthless. In May, 1511, without any known provocation he attacked a certain Natale da Brindisi, a stipendiary of the Pope, and robbed him of money and clothing to the value of seventy ducats. Although he was condemned to banishment, the court order was not carried out. Later that year, in company with his valet, Giacomo da Parma, he attacked a doctor, Prospero da Forzano, who sought refuge from sudden death in the house of a Jew nearby; the Jew's wife was wounded during the quarrel. Giacomo, the servant, paid a fine, but his master escaped scot-free, so powerful were his friends at Bologna.

In 1514 he published his first book—an edition of Mundinus, "per Carpum castigata," printed by Rubiera of Bologna. This edition, in fact, was very little corrected. Yet it represented Berengario's act of faith in the movement against Galenic and Arabic authority in anatomy, a movement which had begun with Mundinus two centuries before, only to yield to the pressure of the old tradition. Mundinus, Berengario, and Vesalius were the new thinkers of Renaissance anatomy, and Berengario forms an important link between the other two scientists. Berengario's edition of Mundinus, insignificant as it is, was much sought after and is now very rare. In its preface he promised to publish another book.

Indeed, between 1514 and 1522 Berengario published all the books upon which his fame is established. He accumulated a large clientele and a fortune, becoming known as a physician among the rich and great far outside Bologna. In 1515 he bought a fine house and some land and, in 1516, a larger house, a palazzo where he could display to better advantage the works of art he had purchased from Cellini and others. Among these treasures was a Roman marble torso, found in December, 1514, in the foundation of a house in Bologna. Berengario bought this statue, worth at least two hundred ducats at that time, for only twenty ducats. The torso is now in the Museo Civico of Bologna.

Lorenzo de' Medici, nephew of Pope Leo X, while fighting against Francesco Maria della Rovere for the possession of the dukedom of Urbino was wounded in the head on March 28, 1517. Among the physicians in attendance upon him at Ancona was Berengario. He carefully describes Lorenzo's occipital fracture in *De fractura cranei* (fol. 23b). The operation (trepanation) was performed by another surgeon, who handled it rather clumsily for lack of the proper instruments. Berengario excuses himself for not bringing his own instruments, since he had been informed too late about the nature of the wound and had to make extreme haste to reach Lorenzo's bedside. Berengario took charge of the postoperative cure of the wound, and Lorenzo returned to Florence completely cured on May 24. The skull of Lorenzo is among the Medici remains in the family chapel in the cathedral of San Lorenzo at Florence. In 1875 these remains were exhumed and examined by two physicians and a journalist, each of whom published an account of the examination. A plaster copy of the skull is to be found in the Anatomical Museum of the University of Florence; Vittorio Putti, in his study of the life and work of Berengario (*Berengario da Carpi* [Bologna: L. Cappelli, 1937]) published photographs of this copy.

Upon his return to Bologna Berengario set to work and in little more than two months completed his book on skull fractures and dedicated it to Lorenzo, to whom Machiavelli only three years before had dedicated *The Prince*. Berengario's chief purpose in writing this book was perhaps to show that he knew more about skull fractures than his colleagues at Ancona in attendance upon Lorenzo. The volume was published in December, 1518, and a second edition in 1535; reprints appeared in 1629, 1651, 1715, and 1729. Putti believes that another edition between those of 1518 and 1535 was printed, but the two mutilated copies of it which exist do not permit an exact dating.

The next event in Berengario's life was a dishonorable one. He was convicted of unlawful possession by invasion of the house and property of Zambelli Petenghi; in his counterplea Berengario falsely and arrogantly claimed on November 29, 1520, that the sentence had been passed during his absence and was therefore null and void. He was allowed to possess the property he had thus stolen on the grounds of his old age, another indication of his power in high places. Putti with justice says of him, "Avarice and cupidity stir in the mind of this great man greater passions than glory or virtue."

During these years of varied experiences Berengario's masterpiece was taking shape in his mind. It had perhaps already begun to emerge with his edition of Mundinus in 1514. The text of Mundinus' *Anatomy* was to serve as a springboard for his own description of anatomy and as an outline which he could follow and amplify. By 1521 the *Commentary on the Anatomy of Mundinus* was completed. Berengario takes issue in it with his great predecessor but preserves the fundamental lines of Mundinus' research, using his own eyes and reason instead of authority alone. When he says in the *Commentary* (fol. 484b) that he had frequently placed all the dried-out vertebrae beneath his gaze as he wrote their description and had always kept the other members before his eyes also, we can conclude, of course, that he attempted to write always from firsthand inspection, difficult as that was in an age when it was impossible to preserve cadavers. Further, he experimented to some extent, injecting water into the bladder of the foetus to discover whether, as Galen and Avicenna said, the foetus urinates through the urachus or umbilicus or, as Berengario held, through the urethra. He also injected water into the emulgent vein in studying the vascular circulation of the kidneys.

The *Commentary* was written with great speed and printed even more rapidly. Its dedication to Cardinal Giulio de' Medici, legate of Bologna and later Pope Clement VII, was a sign of the respect in which Berengario held the Medici family. The Cardinal, among other demonstrations of his favor, had sent Berengario to Piacenza to help cure the *condottiere* Giovanni dalle Bande Nere, also a Medici. Somewhat the same experience as at Ancona with Lorenzo was repeated at Piacenza with Giovanni, the latter preferring the services of the Jewish surgeon lent him by Francesco Gonzaga. Among other important patients Berengario also had the Marchese Galeazzo Pallavicini, a general of French troops (*Commentary,* fol. 180b, and *Isagogae breves,* fol. 16a). The general's gout had been complicated by nephritis, and Berengario describes in detail the quinsy from which Galeazzo suffered and its relief by means of cupping glasses.

In the early years of Clement VII's pontificate Berengario for a second time spent some months at Rome in 1525 and 1526. There he attended a member of the papal curia, Cardinal Pompeo Colonna, who was afflicted with carcinoma. The Cardinal, described by contemporaries as impetuous, proud, very gallant, a man of little religion but unmeasured ambition, had first opposed, then stoutly supported, the candidacy of the new Pope. The hostility thus generated between Clement VII and Pompeo Colonna finally led to open conflict and the Pope's retreat into the Castel Sant' Angelo at Rome in September, 1526. Since the Cardinal lived for six years after Berengario's visit to Rome, it is probable that the carcinoma from which he suffered was not a malignant tumor but some sort of ulcer.

Berengario's meeting with Benvenuto Cellini during 1526 has already been described in the words of the famous artist. Cellini's statement about the Pope's request for the permanent services of Berengario may well be true, for it is known that Clement VII had many doctors, indeed so many that the comic poet Francesco Berni wrote the following epigram on the subject:

> This is a vow that Pope Clemente
> Has paid to the Virgin Mary because
> At one stroke and by a miracle
> She saved him from eight doctors' claws.

From Cellini's description of Berengario there emerges a composite but probably not entirely faithful picture of the man as a great surgeon, learned, well read, with good taste in art, but also a charlatan greedy for gain. His use or misuse of mercury ointment in treating syphilis should not, however, be held so harshly against him as it is by Cellini; many physicians used the same remedy just as fruitlessly in those days. In 1521 Berengario's own publisher, Benedetti of Bologna, published Ulrich Hutten's *De guaiaci medicina et morbo gallico* (first printed at Mainz in 1519).

Vasari (in his *Lives of the Painters* [Rome, 1759], II, 124–25) tells how Cardinal Colonna gave Berengario a "Saint John in the Desert" painted by Raphael in the last years of the painter's life, around 1518. Berengario had asked for this picture as his fee and carried it back to Bologna. Conjectured to be a copy of the Saint John by Raphael in the Uffizzi at Florence, the painting eventually came into the Royal Gallery of Bologna.

Upon his return to Bologna, thus rich and distinguished, apparently at the very pinnacle of his fortunes, Berengario lost his post as Lecturer in Surgery, which he had held for twenty-four years at the university. Scholars have resorted to conjecture in order to explain such an unexpected turn of events in the hitherto remarkably successful career of Berengario. Only a most urgent cause could have made him leave Bologna so suddenly that he did not even collect part of the annual salary due him, as is shown by records for the school year 1526–27.

Fallopio (1523–62) in his book *De morbo gallico* (Padua, 1563) gave rise to the belief that Berengario had been charged with vivisection. He wrote, "This man so hated Spaniards that, when he was at Bologna, he took twin Spaniards suffering from syphilis and determined to practice vivisection on them: being ruined for this reason, he went to Ferrara." Berengario, like Vesalius, was too shrewd to risk such ruin; Fallopio's words must be regarded as an interpolation of the kind which has been found elsewhere in his books. Although Berengario may have hated Spaniards (their troops behaved badly in Carpi in 1522–23), he had a Spanish student named Ochoa Gonzalez whom he loved like a son and to whom he dedicated his edition of some minor works of Galen in 1522. There is probably no truth in the accusation of vivisection, made many years after Berengario's death. It is interesting, however, to note his almost prophetic remarks on vivisection in the *Commentary on the Anatomy of Mundinus* (fol. 4):

In our own time anatomy is not practiced on living bodies except by chance under the hands of physicians, as sometimes happens to me in cutting into abscesses, operating on ulcers, or trepanning and perforating members of the body. . . . And it would be far better to ascertain the truth in live bodies than in dead ones except that we are restrained because of the cruelty this involves.

Among the more probable causes for Berengario's departure from Bologna are the plague, famine, or the invasion of Bourbon troops. The latter cause is likely in view of the fact that Berengario could be considered an adherent of the Bentivoglio and thus *persona non grata* to the invaders. Both his colleagues Achillini and Pomponazzi, who in turn fled from the University of Ferrara, had been forced to suspend their lectures because of invasion by foreign troops. The plague, on the other hand, does not seem to have frightened Berengario, if we are to believe Fallopio. In the latter's *De tumoribus,* chapter xi, he describes Berengario walking about some unnamed city displaying his medicaments to the stricken during the great pestilence of 1527. Berengario's own death has been assigned by some as the reason for the sudden disappearance of his name from the records of the University of Bologna; but his first will is dated at Carpi on March 24, 1528, and he was at Modena in practice on July 27, 1528.

Relations between Berengario and the dukes of Ferrara had long since become most amicable. By 1529 he had been given a grant of land and been made court surgeon to Alfonso D'Este at Ferrara, a city which at this time also controlled Carpi. Always an opportunist and an excellent diplomat, Berengario knew how to win and keep friends on both sides of a political fence who could prove useful in any situation. We may note that in 1529 he edited some works of Galen, revised from the Latin translation of Demetrius Chalcondylus, and dedicated them to Ercole Gonzaga, Cardinal of Mantua, son of Francesco Gonzaga and Isabella D'Este. The book was published at Bologna by Giovan Battista Faelli. Incidentally, Ercole had been a student at Bologna in 1521, had listened to the lectures of Berengario's colleagues Lazzaro Bonamici and Pietro Pomponazzi, and had sought out Berengario himself. Cardinal Pietro Bembo had allowed Berengario to rent for a short time at Bologna some property of his held in lease from the possessions of the Church of San Giovanni Gerosolomitano, another sign of high favor. Apparently the last days of Berengario were to be as fortunate as those of his earlier career.

The exact date of his death is unknown; in this, as in other points, his life bears a remarkable resemblance to that of Vesalius. His will, published in 1880 by Guaitoli and again in 1923 by Martinotti, is a long, involved document now in the Archivio Guaitoli at Carpi. It is dated March 24, 1528. Apart from small and unimportant bequests to his sisters Barbara and Taddea, to his nephews and nieces (whom he provided with dowries), and a few books and instruments bequeathed to Gaspare, his nephew by his sister Giovanna, Berengario made Damiano, son of his brother Giovanni Andrea, his sole heir. By the will, if Damiano died without issue, Berengario's property was to be used as a trust fund for the aid of students in medicine or civil law from the town of Carpi. His books were to be made available also to such students or to be housed in a convent at Carpi. The greater share of the library went to Damiano, but it is probable that the total number of books was small: forty or fifty books in those days constituted a physician's specialized library. Berengario probably knew no Greek except for the few terms which he uses in his writings and certainly no Arabic; his Avicenna was, of course, a Latin translation. No doubt he owned a Latin Aristotle, some works of Hippocrates, and a few of Galen. A Celsus, a Galen, and the Avicenna were among the books left to Gaspare.

Before his will was discovered by Guaitoli, the general belief was that Berengario had left his property to the Duke of Ferrara. This story arose from a passage in Fallopio's *De morbo gallico* in which Berengario's use of mercury ointment was referred to with a statement of his profits—40,000 ducats, raised in a later edition of the book to 50,000. We have already found how untrustworthy the remarks of Fallopio in regard to Berengario could be. No trace of a will leaving his property to the Duke of Ferrara has ever been found; that such a will ever existed is doubtful in view of the fact that no notarial document, certainly necessary in connection with an estate of such proportions, was recorded. It is possible that the Duke of Ferrara took over Berengario's property for himself without informing Berengario's heirs. No public eulogy at Ferrara or Bologna, by university officials or noble patrons, made known the passing of the most illustrious anatomist of his day, the valued friend of popes, cardinals, dukes, and other worthies.

According to Guaitoli, Berengario died in Ferrara on November 24, 1530, and was buried in the Church of San Francesco. The information comes from a document listing important people who were buried in the churches of Ferrara. Putti, however, after his usual careful researches, has found no record of Berengario's burial in San Francesco in the Archbishop's Archives at Ferrara. Possibly the entry concerning Berengario may have been in a lost volume. It is not known in which parish Berengario was residing when he died, unless indeed he died in the Duke's palace. Not all the documents of the Church of San Francesco are located in one place; some are at Modena and some perhaps in the University Library at Ferrara, not labeled for easy reference.

Something further may be said about Berengario's achievements as a teacher and his relations with students. From the records of the University of Bologna it has been discovered that when he was absent from his teaching post and schedule he was not docked in pay as was the prevailing custom for professors in those days. This immunity may have been the result of intercession in his behalf from high places, however, and not a special mark of respect from the university. Berengario was highly regarded by his students, who showed him various signs of affection. The popularity of his classes was proved by a statement in an official university rotulus which compared his status with that of a colleague:

Ad lecturam chirurgie
D. M. Iacobus de Carpo habet sat scholarium.
D. M. Dominicus della Lana nihil valet vel parum.

A note in the margin points out that Dominicus had three students and Berengario ten or twelve. Mention has been made of Hernando Ochoa Gonzalez, a student from Spain to whom Berengario dedicated his edition of some minor works of Galen. This man's name is recorded in the archives of the Collegio di San Clemente degli Spagnuoli at Bologna; he came from Bermeo in Spain.

Another student, an assistant to Berengario, was a German, Johannes Lange, from Löwenberg in Silesia; he studied at Ferrara and attained his doctorate in medicine at Pisa in 1522. He held a practice for forty years at Heidelberg as chief physician to the Electors of the Palatinate and died there in 1565. His book on medicine, written in letter form, *Medicinalium epistolarum miscellanea* (Basel, 1554), described an operation by Berengario at which Lange assisted. The latter brought home to Germany the Italian method of trepanning on the crown of the skull, as he had seen the operation performed by Luigi da Vigo at Rome. The trepanning instrument used was called *abaptiston*, "that which does not dip," or "the unbaptized," taking its meanings from the Greek words *a* plus *baptein*, to dip (see Putti, *op. cit.*, p. 202, for a description). Berengario in his *De fractura cranei* calls it *terebrum non profundans*, a drill which does not pierce the meninges of the skull. German physicians joked with Lange about his instrument, saying that in Germany only children and, at most, church bells were baptized, but at Rome, where the Pope lived, even surgical instruments could be baptized.

Supposedly, two portraits of Berengario exist, but Putti regards both as purely imaginary representations. One is an oil painting in the Museo Municipale at Carpi. It measures 75 by 54 centimeters and is well preserved. The only evidence for the authenticity of this painting, made in the seventeenth or eighteenth century, is the superscription which names him: *Jacobus Berengarius Carpen. Anotom. et Medic. profess. Eximius anno 1495.* The date is enough to show its spurious nature, for Berengario is represented as a suspicious-eyed old man with white beard and hair at a time when he could have been no more than thirty-five. The painting probably forms part of a series, of similar technique and pigments, preserved in the museum at Carpi and provided by some local citizen who wished to adorn the town with portraits, even though fictitious, of local celebrities.

The second portrait is a woodcut in Brambilla's book on the discoveries made by Italian medical men (G. A. Brambilla, *Storia delle scoperte fisico-medico-anatomico-chirurgiche fatte dagli uomini illustri italiani* [Milan, 1780], II, 127). In this chiefly ornamental portrait Berengario's name is misspelled; he is depicted as a dashing, bright-eyed young man with a mustache. The picture is as far from lifelike as are all the other pictures of famous Italian medical men in Brambilla's book. We must conclude from these facts that no authentic portrait of Berengario exists, if indeed one was ever made; none has so far been found.

The place of Berengario in the history of anatomy has never been adequately assessed. Such an assessment would require a thorough study and a translation of the *Commentary on Mundinus,* a study which has not yet been attempted. The *Commentary* is Berengario's most significant contribution to anatomical knowledge, but like many another great book it was too large (527 folio pages), too detailed, too diffusely organized, and perhaps too costly to be successful commercially; only one edition was ever printed. His publisher, Gerolamo Benedetti of Bologna, risked losing even the profit such hazards might allow him by publishing in the next year the *Isagogae breves,* which bears much the same relationship to the *Commentary* as Vesalius' *Epitome* bears to his much larger and more important *De humani corporis fabrica.* This compact little book of only sixty-three quarto folios in the 1535 edition was easy to consult and to carry about in the pocket. It contained a great deal of information, a few details of personal experience in anatomy which could not have been printed in the *Commentary,* and more and better illustrations. The *Isagogae* (1522)—the title means nothing more than "short introduction," using a Latin transliteration from a Greek word—became his best-known work; it was followed in seven months by a second edition (1523) and by others in 1530(?) and 1535. The 1535 edition is called by Putti the fourth, but, as he says and as I have ascertained by collation of the texts, it is chiefly a reprint of the 1522 edition with slightly different woodcuts and two more laudatory verses by friends. In 1660 appeared the first English translation of the *Isagogae breves,* by Henry Jackson of London. Both this translation and its 1664 reissue have been carefully discussed by S. V. Larkey and Linda Tum Suden in *Isis* (Vol. XXI, No. 60 [1934]). The *Isagogae* inaugurated, as Putti indicates, a new era in anatomy and became at once the most authoritative work of its kind until the appearance of Vesalius' *De humani corporis fabrica* (1543). Many anatomists, including Vesalius, borrowed from it, though they sometimes failed to acknowledge their indebtedness.

In the *Isagogae* Berengario gives a concise but extremely detailed account of the anatomy of the human body. He follows the methods of Mundinus in dividing the body into three major cavities and in describing the "members" contained or which in turn contain other members in each cavity, giving comparative relationships by the use of the words "common," "proper," or "more proper." These terms are explained by Berengario in the first pages of his book; the present translator's note on them on page 185 may also be compared. He begins his description with the lower, proceeds to the middle and upper cavities, and ends with the extremities. The picturesque terminology of Mundinus, listed in a glossary by Charles Singer (*The*

"*Fasciculo di Medicina,*" *Venice, 1493: A Translation of the "Anathomia"* *of Mondino da Luzzi, Monumenta Medica,* Vol. II [Milan: R. Lier, 1924]), is reproduced with the addition of many parallel terms from Greek, Latin, and Arabic; sometimes Berengario uses the very phrases of Mundinus. His dependence on his distinguished predecessor is clear, but he expanded his treatment of anatomy to include a great deal that Mundinus omitted or ignored. Thus the anatomy of Berengario is the first full-scale description of the entire human body between that of Mundinus, who wrote in 1326, and that of Vesalius, in 1543.

Berengario's dependence on authorities other than Mundinus, whom he frequently mentions, especially in connection with his *Commentary,* is also considerable and consistently acknowledged by exact reference to books and chapters; he sometimes differs with his authorities, as with Avicenna on the fourth part of the blood in the middle ventricle of the heart, something Berengario said he could not see with his own eyes. He quotes Aristotle, Celsus, Galen, and Avicenna, and refers to other medical men, such as Herophilus; he mentions no works of contemporaries. Vesalius, it may be pointed out, refers to no one but Galen and Asclepius in the *Epitome* and then only to criticize.

Berengario uses Arabic terms freely; Putti believes he knew the Arabic works thoroughly in their Latin translations. Berengario even made a judgment on an important bibliographical problem in the history of Persian medicine which has been corroborated by modern research (Putti, *Berengario da Carpi,* pp. 256–57). Berengario makes much use, as did Galen and the early anatomists, of homology and analogy among the organs, as in the case of the uterus and penis, and of Aristotelian teleology, categories, and properties in describing the parts of the body.

In its scope the *Isagogae* is much more detailed than Vesalius' *Epitome,* a book which was written to serve the same purpose: that of a concise anatomical manual. As a sample of its greater thoroughness, we can compare the anatomy of the heart and lungs given by each. Vesalius reduces both heart and lungs with their vascular system into five pages of my translation of the *Epitome;* Berengario uses the equivalent of at least thirteen pages of typescript for the purpose. Vesalius does not lead up to the description of these organs with a careful discussion of the diaphragm, mediastinum, and pericardium as does Berengario; his procedure is much more abrupt and lacking in smooth transitions. Vesalius says nothing about comparative anatomy, cites no authority, leaves out all homologies or parallels even of a useful kind, such as the comparison of the heart's shape to that of a pyramid; he presents a severely truncated view of the heart's relation to the organs around it. He does not recognize the three right lobes of the lung; Berengario describes them carefully. Vesalius abandons the old custom fol-

lowed by Mundinus and Berengario of patiently listing for each organ the
main facts about its substance, size, shape, location, connections, and complexion; his writing loses breadth and depth thereby in the same manner
in which the modern medical dictionaries have lost much of their linguistic,
cultural, and humanistic values by dropping the old terms and descriptions
which can still be found in Dunglison's *A Dictionary of Medical Science*
(Philadelphia, 1874). Berengario gives such details, recapitulating them at
the end of each organ's description, and though some of these are of no great
importance ("complexion" is a vague and rather picturesque term without
much scientific value, but it does suggest something of the bodily habit of
each organ), the result is systematic and more satisfying than Vesalius'
sketchy accounts. One feels that Berengario attempted to cover all possible
points that require description. The veins of both heart and lung are discussed in detail by Berengario; although Vesalius is careful with these, he
omits discussion of the lung's fistulae and gives a bare outline of the ostiola
of the cardiac vessels. Both use the old theory of mixed blood and air passing
to the heart in veins and arteries, but even here Berengario is more explicit,
carrying out to its full conclusions the false hypothesis in which all anatomists
of his time believed. Vesalius postpones to another chapter the explanation
of what happens to the small part of air drawn to the brain; Berengario
explains in its proper context the passage of this air through the rete mirabile
and its transformation into animal spirit. Vesalius, for all his prestige and
his undeniable contribution to anatomical science, did not advance beyond
the theories of humors, spirits (vital, animal, and natural), and heart action
accepted by anatomists down to his own time. In fact, the humoral pathology
was not completely exploded until the actual establishment of the nature of
oxygen by Lavoisier in 1775.

The *Isagogae breves* is a descriptive anatomy, a brief geography of the
human body, in which by teleological etymologies is presented an onoma-
tology actually less complicated and less Latinized than that of modern
anatomical terminology. For example, one will find nowhere in this book
such cumbersome, although accurate, phrases as "flexor carpi radialis" or
"quadratus labii superioris." Berengario's book has certain traits of the
Mondinian school of dissection. One of the most significant of these is the
use of frequent Arabic terms; these are occasionally given as the chief term
of a group, taking precedence over the Latin and Greek words. We can see
in this book perhaps more clearly than in any other of the time the transition
from medieval anatomy, with its heavy dependence on the work of the
Arabs, to the anatomy of the Renaissance, which only a few years later takes
full shape in the work of Vesalius.

The book is also, of course, a manual of dissection. Berengario takes pains
to instruct his readers where and how to cut the cadaver most expeditiously,

mentioning the instruments needed and telling his reader which parts to lay aside for further examination, "for the sake of a better order." His practical experience as a surgeon is utilized in his descriptions; at least two episodes, his treatment in company with other physicians of quinsy and of diseased uterus, are presented with names, dates, and other details like a modern case history. Frequent references to his *Commentary on Mundinus* stamp the *Isagogae breves* as a student guide and no more; a more complete discussion on all subjects was to be found in the larger book.

The final summary for each member of the accepted categories—size, number, connections, position, complexion, and so on—is often perfunctory, as such a fixed system of reference would imply. It is, nevertheless, a convenient recapitulation and in one detail perhaps of more far-reaching importance than might at first appear. His carefully recorded connections for members, to the liver by veins, to the heart by arteries, and to the brain by nerves, is a consistent attempt to place the specific member in its configurational relationship to the entire body and has certain physiological and even pathological implications which are hinted at in the all-too-brief listing of the ills to which each member is subject.

There is no doubt that, from the point of view of simplicity and ease of learning, Berengario's approach by separate members together with their veins, arteries, cartilages, panniculi, tendons, and their functions is more practical than that of Vesalius, who in the *Epitome* lumped all the ligaments of all the members into one section with the muscles and all the bones and cartilages into another, irrespective of the members they served. This approach complicates unnecessarily the problem of learning. The description of members and their features in association on the basis of regional relations instead of in separate listings of parts is more easily grasped by the student. The enumeration of parts as followed by Vesalius has now been dropped in modern anatomical teaching except for the enumeration of the twelve cranial nerves.

I should point out again most emphatically that any statement of the full contributions of Berengario to anatomical science must take into consideration his largest and most important work, the *Commentary on Mundinus*. It was the repository of his most mature judgment, and the next step in Berengarian studies is its translation. According to Putti's list, seven copies of it exist: one each in Carpi (Biblioteca Comunale), Bologna (Biblioteca Comunale), Modena (Biblioteca Estense), British Museum, New York Academy of Medicine, the Surgeon-General's Library, and in Putti's possession. An eighth copy belongs to the Department of Anatomy, University of Maryland, Baltimore.

Although no thorough scientific study of Berengario's work exists, we nevertheless find that modern authorities give him high praise. I have assembled a few of their judgments here. Charles Singer, for example, says that the earliest improvement on the medieval account of the brain is to be found in the *Isagogae* of 1522. Arturo Castiglioni enlarges on this to state that Berengario described the lateral ventricles of the brain, presumably the first to do so. He also says that Berengario gave the first careful descriptions of the sphenoid sinuses, the vermiform appendix, the tympanum, the thymus gland, the arytenoid cartilages, the pineal gland and its position in regard to the third ventricle of the brain, the action of cardiac valves, and the vocal organs. Berengario himself says Mundinus did not know the sciatic nerve; the assumption is that Berengario himself was the first to describe it. Fielding H. Garrison declares that Berengario was the first to substitute drawing from nature for traditional schemata, was a pioneer in the simple treatment of gunshot wounds, and was the first to fill the blood vessels with fluid (tepid water) in order to study circulation. Vittorio Putti insists that Berengario was the first to discover that the cavity of the uterus is not divided into two or seven compartments, as Galen and his followers believed, but "has one single cavity or cell."

Charles Singer, in a recent work on Vesalius' description of the brain, states flatly: "Of all Western anatomical works before Vesalius only those of Berengario and Massa are firmly based on experience."

Karl Sudhoff regarded the representation of the abdominal muscles in the *Commentary* as an advance of a distinguished kind in their description ("Die Bauchmuskelzeichnung von 1496," *Archiv für Geschichte der Medizin,* III [1910], 134). Holl believed that Berengario was the discoverer of the papillae of the kidneys ("Vesals Darstellung des Baues der Niere," *Archiv für Geschichte der Medizin,* VI [1912], 135). Berengario was the first to admit frankly that the pores in the septum separating the ventricles of the heart are not completely visible in man, according to Charles Greene Cumston (*An Introduction to the History of Medicine* [1926], p. 271).

Ralph Major, in his *History of Medicine* (1954), says that Berengario was the first anatomist of his time to distinguish the chyliferous ducts from the veins and to describe a horseshoe kidney. He was also "responsible for the term vas deferens, attacked by purists as a misnomer since the prefix *de* indicates down, whereas the vas leads up." The statement about the horseshoe kidney is doubtless based on the important article by John A. Benjamin and Dorothy M. Schullian ("Observations on Fused Kidneys with Horseshoe Configuration: The Contribution of Leonardo Botallo [1564]," *Journal of the History of Medicine,* V [1950], 315). They translate the passage in question at folio 17b (*Isagogae breves,* 1523) and declare, "Berengario da Carpi, it appears, was among the first to write on this subject." On page 316 of this article the authors present a figure showing the composite diagrammatic representation of the probable anatomical findings of Berengario on the horseshoe kidney. Botallo, in his later and more complete description of this anomaly, does not mention Berengario.

George W. Corner believes that Berengario introduced the distrust of authority into sixteenth-century anatomy. A. C. Crombie concurs with Lynn Thorndike in emphasizing the statement in *Commentary,* folio 260, about his experiment (parallel to that with the kidney) to prove that the bladder of a nine-months' unborn child had no opening other than the urinary pores. Finally, Singer, on Berengario's *Commentary,* declares, "It is at many points both critical and original and undoubtedly a foundation work of modern anatomy."

The most determined effort yet made to destroy the reputation of Berengario and to diminish his standing in the history of anatomy was made by Moritz Roth in his famous book on Vesalius (*Andreas Vesalius Bruxellensis* [Berlin, 1892]). It is clear that the purpose of Roth's first chapter on pre-Vesalian anatomy is to reduce as much as possible the prestige and the contributions of all previous anatomical research in order to elevate his hero. Roth's enthusiasm has fostered among modern scientists an undue and unrealistic veneration for Vesalius; the time has long been ripe for a new and more balanced approach to his life and work.

Roth calls Berengario the most industrious and most important dissector before Vesalius, with his dissections attended by more than five hundred students and a number of citizens besides. But he charges that in public dissections Berengario omitted the dissection of most of the muscles, taking his evidence from Berengario's own admission of this fact in *Commentary,* folio 516a. Berengario also declared that in such public dissections he examined the extremities and the skeleton only cursorily (*ibid.,* fol. 438a). It should be said that in the *Isagogae breves* Berengario frequently makes the distinction between public and private dissections, saying that it was difficult to show the more complicated parts of the body in public dissection: some allowance for such practical difficulties should also have been made by Roth. Berengario's books, according to Roth, are written in barbarous Latin; their author shows himself to be credulous, superstitious, and vain. He ascribes divine genius to his master Mundinus, whose work, *because of its form and brevity* (italics mine), he preferred to that of Aristotle, Galen, Avicenna, and the anatomists of the Renaissance.

The charge of barbarous Latin is too severe. The style of the *Commentary* and of the *Isagogae breves,* both 1523 and 1535 editions, is serviceable and clear, if not brilliant. Their language and style are naturally adapted to a very practical purpose.

Although Berengario revered Mundinus, he also honored Aristotle and Galen, as he showed by citing them frequently; further, he recognized that Avicenna plagiarized much from Haly Abbas, an indication that he was critical of his sources among the anatomical writers. Berengario used some works of Galen which Roth considers unimportant, including spurious writings such as *De anatomia vivorum* and *De motibus liquidis*. One work cited by Galen and later by Berengario is not even extant: *De dissonantia anatomicorum*. Of this, the first book is mentioned by Galen in *De administrationibus anatomicis* i. 4. On the other hand, Berengario recognizes the *De anatomia vivorum* as spurious or as the work of a second Galen (*Commentary*, fols. 216a, 216b). *De usu partium humani corporis*, the work Berengario cites most often, is certainly not the least important of Galen's writings.

Berengario is, in Roth's opinion, a dialectician and compiler who does not deserve Gabriele Fallopio's praise. Among other things, Fallopio says, "These [middle ear ossicles] were unknown to the ancient anatomists, and the first to bring them into the light was Jacopo of Carpi, also beyond all doubt the first restorer of the art of anatomy, which Vesalius afterward perfected" (*Observationes anatomicae*, p. 25).

Roth further insists that Berengario's occasional claims to discoveries, modestly expressed as they are, were not backed up by firsthand observation and were made subject to the opinion of his authorities. For example, Berengario writes: "I refer this opinion of mine to the learned. . . . I submit because I do not wish to be vainglorious concerning the discovery of any member of the body of which so many and so great experts and physicians and philosophers have made no mention" (*Commentary*, fol. 466a; see similar passages collected by Roth, *op. cit.*, p. 43).

Roth also charges that Berengario allowed an imaginary anatomy to exist alongside the anatomy perceived by the senses. He bases this statement on Berengario's attitude toward the rete mirabile and the supposed hollowness of the optic nerve. In the *Commentary* Berengario fences with Galen on these matters without actually rejecting the anatomical features involved. It should be pointed out, however, that in almost every instance Roth takes his evidence for Berengario's reluctance to abandon these absurdities from the *Commentary*. In the 1535 *Isagogae breves* Berengario reveals a change of mind, declaring that neither the hollowness (or perforation) of the optic nerve nor the rete mirabile has been perceived by him. Berengario often refers his readers to the *Commentary* for further details, omitting his earlier erroneous views from the text, without specifically stating that his position has changed. Roth ignores this fact.

Roth's explanation of Berengario's unwillingness or inability to break with tradition and push forward from doubt to a positive stand is not convincing. He believes Berengario was hesitant even when he suspected the truth because his method of work all too rarely included experiment. He seems to forget such items as Berengario's observations on water contained in the pericardium in his vivisection of an animal. As he says, "I dissected live animals, and immediately upon my first attempt while the animal still lived I wished to see the pericardium, and I saw much water in it while the motion of the heart was still strong. From this I infer that this water always exists in the pericardium of a healthy animal" (on the fluid of the brain, *Commentary*, fol. 439a; nothing is said of the pericardial fluid, however, in the discussion of the capsule of the heart, fol. 336).

Although Roth will not accept Berengario as the reformer of anatomy, he admits that he and his anti-Galenic contemporaries, the Aristotelian anatomists of Italy, held fast to dissection of the human body and brought authority into doubt by the constant use of the evidence of the senses. They thus advanced the process of founding anatomy on a firm basis. They gave Vesalius the opportunity to work with a sympathetic audience willing and eager to hear the truth. Roth's index references to Berengario run to more than sixty; his criticisms extend to Berengario's pictorial representations of the human body. The fact that Vesalius also copied his predecessors in both anatomical theory and in pictures (the third muscle figure, for example, of the *Fabrica* shows similarity to the wound man of the *Fasciculus medicinae* [1493]) reduces the impact of Roth's assertions.

It is one of the ironies of history that Vesalius himself was similarly attacked, after his death, by Eustachius and Fabricius ab Aquapendente among others. Like him, Berengario had his defenders, beginning with Fallopio, the student and successor of Vesalius, and Eustachius, who wrote: "Jacopo of Carpi, surgeon and anatomist, is not so to be scorned, although certain most ungrateful men later plundered his work, and in order that he should be belittled by all, they did not blush to call him the dregs of anatomists" (*Opuscula anat.*, p. 153). The final insult is that of Vesalius (*Fabrica*, 1543, v. 15. 531. 8; ii. 7. 278. 5), made, of course, without naming his victim directly. Jean Riolan, *fils, Opera anatomica* (Paris, 1649), not only attacked Vesalius but defended Berengario, saying among other things that Berengario had discovered the vermiform process before Vesalius was born (*Anthropographie* ii. 14. 102). Finally, although Roth's attack, determined as it is, cannot be considered successful, it must be included in any future full-scale estimation of Berengario's contributions to the history of anatomy. All such groundless insults as Vesalius', however, should be carefully deleted from the record and, in turn, precautions taken not to exalt Berengario beyond his just deserts. When the task is undertaken by some future historian of medicine, perhaps this translation of the *Isagogae breves* and the material collected in conjunction with it may be of some small service.

For a more charitable view of Berengario than Roth's we turn to Lynn Thorndike. In his chapter on "Anatomy from Carpi to Vesalius" (*A History of Magic and Experimental Science* [1941], V, 498–531) he defends Berengario's role as commentator on Mundinus and as a follower of authority.

From the same source that Roth used, the *Commentary,* Thorndike draws more encouraging conclusions. He points out that Berengario insisted that he followed Galen except where his own observation was at variance with Galen's views. Berengario also praised Mundinus for his brevity but admitted that his predecessor was sometimes in error. It is worth noting that Mundinus also was unfairly criticized by ignorant and careless writers of the first half of the sixteenth century, by Conrad Gesner and Leonhart Fuchs for example, both of whom knew less anatomy than Mundinus. Perhaps this is the beginning of that unpleasant practice of the northern, especially German, anatomists: the belittling of Italian anatomists, a practice which has tended to obscure pre-Harveian Italian contributions to the discovery of the heart's circulation.

Berengario's deep interest in textual criticism and his wide knowledge of the anatomical literature—Greek, Latin, Arabic, and Italian—are emphasized by Thorndike, who lists many writers mentioned by Berengario. The latter's observations are often acute but not pedantic and narrow. He relied "first and foremost upon his own observations and experience." As to taking credit for discoveries, I should like to underline at this point the fact that nothing in the *Commentary* and only one sentence in the *Isagogae breves* could give any basis to Roth's charge of vanity. The one sentence is (fol. 8b): "On account of this book [the *Commentary*] envy will love me after death," a statement which in the light of later history was absolutely true. Time and again, however, Berengario made his assertions in the most modest manner; even Roth records some of these.

In fact, as Thorndike proceeds to show, merely by quoting the *Commentary,* Berengario was highly skeptical of such views as the one held by Zerbi (the most criticized author mentioned in the *Commentary*) that there was a sieve in the kidneys; of those who believed the os sacrum was in the breast; of the younger men who held that the womb was divided into cells. By constant reference to personal observation on the basis of many dissections, Berengario comments sensibly on the treatment of wounds, the fat of human hearts, operation for bladder stone, unskilful tampering with saliva outlets, half-dead foetuses, monstrous births, medical versus astrological explanations of certain phenomena, the supposed indication—from nodes on the umbilicus of the first-born—of how many children the mother would have, the greater thickness of skull in those who went about hatless, dolichocephalic and brachiocephalic people, etc. He discounted on the grounds of sheer improbability the existence of a prehistoric giant reportedly found near Drepanum, Sicily, a tale recorded in Boccaccio *De genealogia deorum* iv. 68. In the *De fractura cranei* Berengario continued his impressive citation of authorities, showing a mastery of the literature on skull fractures.

Berengario's criticism of authorities led to a small controversy not hitherto noticed by any student of his work, with which I may conclude this tentative account of his status in the history of anatomy. His discussion of the use of anatomical terms by Nicolaus Leonicenus (1428–1524), teacher of Paracelsus and the "best critic of his period" (Castiglioni), brought a reply from that tireless translator and commentator which assumed almost the proportions of a polemic. Leonicenus had published a translation into Latin of Galen's comments on the aphorisms of Hippocrates. Both his former student Johannes Mainardus and Berengario, politely although adversely, had criticized this book. Berengario dealt with it in the *Commentary,* analyzing Leonicenus' interpretation of Galen's discussion of the omentum. Leonicenus had said that the omentum would putrefy if it were extruded beyond the peritoneum. Berengario denied that Galen had said this, declaring that in "girbal" herniae the omentum always passed beyond the interior membrane of the abdomen and never putrefied, a fact he had proved to the satisfaction of his listeners. He preferred to believe that Leonicenus' error arose from a misprint and proceeded to discuss the ancient terms for the parts involved. Leonicenus at once took issue with Berengario and produced a small quarto pamphlet of seventy pages, beautifully printed by Jacopo Pentio de Leuco at Venice in 1522, under the title *Nicolai Leoniceni medici clarissimi contra obtrectatores apologia* (copy in the Clendening Collection, University of Kansas Medical School Library). This answer to Berengario gave rise to a detailed discussion of anatomical nomenclature employed in current Latin translations from Galen. Berengario's further criticism of Leonicenus' view that Galen was not the author of *De iuvamentis membrorum* and on many other points dealing with Leonicenus' treatise on the errors of Pliny (*Commentary,* fols. 89v, 105v, 116v, 361v, 376v–77v, 388v) constituted another source of annoyance for Leonicenus, who extended all his philological powers in defense of his position. His little booklet, now almost forgotten, is only one more indication of the vigorous and often acrimonious differences of opinion that made the study of anatomy so exciting in the Renaissance, in this field as in all others the age of intellectual controversy. In this aspect, too, of the culture of his time Berengario played a distinguished role. Whatever further scholarship may have to say about his work and his contributions, his ability as a polemicist will not be disregarded. It is as a pioneer of far-reaching significance, as the enduring link between medieval and Renaissance anatomy that future ages will look upon Berengario da Carpi.

THE ILLUSTRATIONS

The fame of Vesalius' *Tabulae sex* and of the great illustrations of the *Epitome* and *Fabrica* has tended to obscure the importance of the anatomical pictures originated by his predecessors. Berengario must be considered one of the most distinctive of these. Albrecht von Haller, the founder of the history of anatomical illustration, called him the first to prepare anatomical designs; this statement is echoed by F. H. Garrison, who says Berengario was the first to substitute drawing from nature for traditional schemata. Both the *Commentary* and the *Isagogae breves* appear among the eleven major "graphic incunabula" of pre-Vesalian medical illustration listed by Garrison in his history of medicine. Karl Sudhoff, in a classic study, surmised that all these illustrations derive along narrow lines of mutual imitation from manuscript sketches, sometimes from far-distant non-European lands. It is curious to note that in Italy, a nation of great artists throughout the Middle Ages and the Renaissance, anatomical illustration should nevertheless have lagged so long in reaching standards of true excellence. As Putti observes, the reason must have been that the anatomist (except in the solitary person of Leonardo da Vinci, who had little contemporary influence in this field) was not himself an artist and, being uncertain of the actual anatomical facts, could not guide the hand of the artist, at least until the fortunate meeting of Vesalius and Stephan van Calcar.

Putti (*op. cit.,* pp. 165–99) has carefully discussed the use of anatomical illustration by Berengario. Although all his books carried illustrations, the *Commentary on Mundinus* and the two editions of the *Isagogae breves* prepared during his lifetime are particularly rich in woodcuts. As the knowledge of anatomy grew, there increased with it the need for more minute and accurate illustration, since words in this branch of science, more than in any other, are worth much less than good pictures, a fact Leonardo had recognized and stated clearly in his writings.

Eleven of the twenty-one illustrations of the *Commentary* are of the superficial mantle of muscles. This abundance is traced to the fact that, next to the skeleton, the muscles would be preserved longer for study than the other parts of the body. The artists of the time also profited from such pictures, as Berengario himself pointed out when he said (*Isagogae breves,* fol. 61v): "These figures also assist painters in delineating the members," in his annotation of the picture showing the muscles of the back. The external medicine of the period as practiced by surgeons was also aided by these illustrations; Berengario noted this in his comment on the muscle figure of the lateral regions (fol. 61r).

The six figures of the abdominal muscles in the *Commentary* have their predecessors in the *Conciliator* of 1496 (by Pietro d'Abano, the Averroist heretic, 1250–1316), a book much used down to the seventeenth century. Berengario's figures far surpass, however, the two figures of the *Conciliator* in artistic value and scientific precision. They have a sweetness and grace that indicate a certain harmony with their attitudes of martyrdom; one of them even has an aureole of sunbeams behind him, like Goethe's own drawing of the *Erdgeist* in *Faust*. The man who illustrates the muscles of the lateral regions grandly points into a distance of clouds and trees like a figure by Tintoretto. The harsher figures of the crucified man and the marasmic man were omitted from the 1523 and subsequent editions, no doubt in deference to humanitarian as well as artistic scruples.

Putti remarks in his analysis of the bone and muscle figures, which represent the majority of pictures in the *Isagogae breves,* that no one before Berengario had produced the design of an isolated vertebra such as the second cervical (epistropheus) illustrated in folio 64r of the 1523 edition. He also regards the last figure of the abdominal muscles (fol. 9v) as the first example of a composite figure similar to those used at the present time to show the crossing of muscle fibers and the superficial veins of the arms in the same picture. A remarkable development in the improved figures of the lateral muscles is analyzed by Putti in that figure of the *Commentary* who holds a piece of wood against his right knee but who is changed for the dynamic old man with his staff and windblown hair who strides along in front of a building (*Isagogae breves,* 1522). The final product in this threefold improvement is the seated figure pointing at the clouds of *Isagogae breves,* 1523. The standards of Berengario and his exactions from the artist are indicated in this progression (Putti, figs. 8, 12, 13).

The skeleton is next to the muscles in abundance of illustration. There are four skeletal figures in the *Commentary* and in the 1522 *Isagogae breves* and five in the 1523 *Isagogae breves.* The two figures on folios 71v and 72r (1523) are so poorly executed that they seem to have been made by another hand than that which produced the muscle figures. However, in reference to these figures as well as elsewhere, Putti successfully refutes Moritz Roth's charges that there are contradictions between the text and the figures and that Berengario plagiarized his illustrations. Roth's views arise from his obvious attempts to elevate Vesalius at the expense of Berengario; he forgets that he himself attributes to Vesalius the glory of having so harshly mistreated Galen. Raffaele Caverni remarks in this respect that "Vesalius had as his principal teachers Galen and Berengario, although in order not to appear the disciple of either he covers the latter under the shadow of silence and the former under a heap of insults."

Berengario sought to improve his illustrations by substituting in the 1523 edition of the *Isagogae breves* better figures than those he had used in either the *Commentary* or the 1522 *Isagogae breves,* especially for the uterus, where again a distinct development can be traced. Much depended, of course, on the anatomical example from which these pictures were drawn, a difficult problem to solve in those days when preservatives were not available. Berengario realized that even the best figures he could provide would be hard to interpret for all who were not "talented and expert in lines and shadow, as in a picture." Nevertheless, the Berengarian representations of the uterus were copied by other scientists down to 1682. The only difference between the pictures used by Vesalius and Berengario is that in those of Berengario the ovaries are placed between the horns of the uterus but in the Vesalian *Tabulae anatomicae* (1538) they are continued with the tubes which are detached from the two upper corners of the uterus.

The figures of the veins of the arms and legs are also unsurpassed by any before Berengario's time. The representations of the brain and heart in the 1523 *Isagogae breves* were the first of such excellence to appear, with the exception of Lorenz Phryesen's picture of the brain in his *Spiegel der Artzny* (Strasbourg, 1518). Berengario's representation of the heart, despite its errors, is the best down to his time—only the most insignificant pictures of the heart had been printed before 1523—and Vesalius in the *Tabulae anatomicae* did not improve on Berengario's figure.

The iconography of Berengario's books justly deserves the praise that Putti gives it. Its influence was wide and salutary, remaining even after Vesalius' productions were known. The latter were heavily indebted to Berengario. A question arises: Who was Berengario's artist? Tiraboschi constructed the hypothesis that he was Ugo da Carpi, but Putti believes that the work of at least three different, although anonymous, artists is involved. The pictures in the *Commentary* are by one hand; those in the 1522 *Isagogae breves* are by another, more free and imaginative, who places his figures within a fairly complex landscape, as van Calcar was later to place his figures in the *Fabrica*. In the 1523 *Isagogae breves* Berengario dropped two figures of the uterus and had the third redone. Probably he was impelled to issue the second edition so soon after the first because he wished to offer new pictures for those with which he was dissatisfied rather than because the first edition was exhausted; at least this is Putti's view. Certainly the 1523 edition was, as Berengario said at its close, "more carefully pictured than before." Possibly the design of the spinal column in all its forms of development in the three books was made by Berengario himself. L. Servolini believes that Ugo da Carpi, a noted xylographer contemporary with Berengario, made the woodcuts in Berengario's books but that they were artistically retouched by a better hand. Ugo did not make the original designs; he simply cut them out of the wood blocks. The artist or artists who were chosen, probably by Benedetti the publisher, to make these designs were among those men who worked at Bologna in the first quarter of the sixteenth century, perhaps one of those who created the frontispieces for Benedetti's publications, such as that for a small book entitled *Triomphi de gli mirandi Spettaculi,* etc. (Bologna, 1519), in whose figures Putti sees an affinity of style with the figures in Berengario's books.

A final word—Charles Singer's—may be added on the problem of the artist. In a useful article called "Notes on Renaissance Artists and Practical Anatomy" (*Journal of the History of Medicine,* V [1950], 158) he writes:

There has been much discussion as to whether Leonardo influenced later anatomists. . . . Leonardo was specially active in anatomical work between 1489 and 1513. During precisely this period the anatomical outlook in Italy turned from its medieval phase. The illustrations of the book of Berengario (see no. 12) are not copied from Leonardo but they are among the first attempts to employ the new art in the service of dissectional anatomy. In that sense Berengario's artist was the heir of Leonardo. . . .

12. We must include here one at least of the artists of Berengario's *Isagogae breves* of 1522 and 1523. This was the first anatomical textbook that was illustrated in our modern sense. The representations of internal organs are on a low technical level, certain other of the figures are skillfully drawn from the life, yet others are able studies of écorchés. The figure illustrating the oblique abdominal muscles is very dramatic and has undoubted beauty; that of the pregnant woman is a fine study of *deliquium animae;* several of the écorchés are by one familiar with corresponding representations by the great artists. This work is thus the first to bring the art tradition of its day to the service of anatomical science. As regards illustration it is a not wholly unworthy successor of the *Fasciculo di Medicina* of 1493, nor an entirely negligible predecessor of the *Fabrica* of Vesalius. Could the artist have been Rosso de Rossi?

13. *Rosso de Rossi* (1496–1541) was born at Florence, was a pupil of Andrea del Sarto, and died by his own hand at Fontainebleau where he had been brought by Francis I. To him have been ascribed some of the figures in Charles Estienne's work on anatomy. That book, though not published till 1545, when de Rossi had been four years in his grave, was in preparation as early as 1530. Vasari states that de Rossi had completed a treatise on anatomy before he left Italy in 1530. This never appeared, but Vasari possessed several of de Rossi's sketches. One of his drawings was engraved by de Rossi's pupil Dominico Barbieri (1506–1560) who worked with him at Fontainebleau. It represents two skeletons and two écorchés, each shown from front and back. From it we should guess that the lost anatomical work was for artists.

Although the edition of 1535 has better illustrations than the 1523 edition, it lacks entirely certain ones which appear in the earlier book. It does not have the three plates with five pictures of the heart, folios 31v, 32r, and 32v; it lacks the two pictures of the brain, both of the dura mater and embotum, folio 56, all in the 1523 edition. The latter, however, has only two pictures of the uterus, one of a woman in a chair with a small landscape in the upper left-hand corner of the plate, the other with three separate views of the uterus on one plate; the 1535 edition has four plates for the uterus. In addition there are two plates of the spinal column in the earlier edition, one of which shows the dens and os caudae; the 1535 edition has only one plate.

THE TRANSLATION

The *Isagogae breves* has been translated once before, by Henry Jackson of London, in 1660, reissued with a different address for the same printer, Livewell Chapman, in 1664. The title runs in the leisurely fashion of the time as follows: *"Microcosmographia* [in Greek letters]: or, a Description of the Little World or Body of Man, Being a brief and practical Anatomy of the Body of Man; not only shewing a Methodical description of the parts, but also the manner of Anatomizing from part to part; the like of which hath not been set forth in the English Tongue; Adorned with many plain demonstrative figures. Which was long since composed in Latine, by that famous Jacobus Berengarius of Carpus, Doctor of Arts and Physick, and Reader of Chirurgery in the University of Bononia; and now done into English, and published for Publick use, by Henry Jackson Chirurgeon. By whom is also added a fit Etymon to the Names of the parts in their proper place."

Putti calls this an *edizione;* it is, of course, a translation and nothing more; no Latin text is included and only scattered marginal etymologies. The dedicatory letter to Alberto Pio is omitted. Jackson's version is both picturesque and literal. He leaves many Latin terms untranslated and even transliterates Berengario's *colligantia* ("connection") as "colligancy," which he uses throughout. The translation is remarkably close and well done. Thomas Wharton's letter to the reader contains a brief contemporary estimate of Berengario and high praise for the two famous English physicians of the day, Harvey and Glisson. S. V. Larkey and L. Tum Suden have concluded, from the title page and illustrations of this translation, that Jackson used either the 1522 or the 1535 edition of Berengario's book.

Putti's statement (*op. cit.,* p. 156) that the 1535 edition can be considered a reprint of the 1522 edition is fully borne out by the facts. I have collated the Yale University Medical Historical Library copy of the 1522 edition. Few people have seen this edition, since it is now impossible to find on the book market; single copies exist in the Biblioteca Estense at Modena, in the Staatsbibliothek at Vienna, the Biblioteca Lancisiana at Rome, in Vittorio Putti's possession, and at Yale, a total of five. Since no thorough collation of the editions of the *Isagogae breves* in the Latin text seems to have been made, or at least published (obvious differences in title pages, illustrations, and dedicatory verses have, of course, been noted), I can now state that the 1523 edition is the most complete of all the editions and that all important textual differences lie between the 1523 edition and the edition of 1535, which, since it appeared after the death of Berengario, represents not his last word on the text but his first, being a return to the 1522 text. At least thirteen copies of the 1535 edition are extant: two in Bologna, one in Modena, one in Carpi, one in Paris, two in Washington (the Library of Congress and the Surgeon-General's Library), one in Signor Putti's collection, one at Yale, one at Harvard, one owned by Dr. Robert J. Moes, and one in the possession of Dr. Ralph Major. The thirteenth copy lies at present in Bernard Quaritch's bookstore in London. Neither the British Museum nor the Library of Congress possesses a first edition or a 1523 edition. I have not made an exhaustive search for other copies of the 1535 edition, although they may of course exist, but list only those recorded by Putti in his tentative bibliography and those known to me from other sources.

It is clear from my collation of the 1523 and 1535 editions that Berengario either changed his mind about certain statements made in the earlier edition or preferred not to risk making a definite judgment; sometimes the rejected passage was, of course, a minor repetition. Almost all differences between these editions consist of omissions in the 1535 edition, which I have restored in parentheses in the translation so that the reading of both editions may be seen in the context. In a single instance, the account of his nephew's extraction of a diseased uterus, Berengario corrected the date of writing forward from 1522 to 1523 and added a few more details about the patient. In another instance the 1535 edition contains a passage that does not appear in the 1522, and I have so indicated the fact by a bracketed interpolation.

This introduction to a translation entirely new and intended for the modern reader, with notes both textual and anatomical, has attempted to offer in brief form all the available pertinent facts about Berengario's life and works; very little seems to have been written on him in any language, as the short bibliography indicates. In the translation itself, to repeat, I have interpolated Latin words and English explanations or paraphrases in brackets; the additions in parentheses translate all the material contained in the 1523 edition which does not appear in the 1522 edition or its reprint, the so-called 1535 edition. It can be seen from these additions how Berengario changed his mind or qualified statements made in the first edition. Since he was dead by 1530, it is difficult to discover what part he may have played in the publication of the 1535 edition.

A
SHORT INTRODUCTION
TO
ANATOMY
(ISAGOGAE BREVES)

THE ANATOMY OF CARPI

A SHORT INTRODUCTION

VERY CLEAR AND FULL, TO THE ANATOMY OF THE HUMAN
BODY, FOR USE BY THE COMMON FELLOWSHIP
OF PHYSICIANS, GIVEN FORTH TO THE
LIGHT AT THE WISHES OF HIS
STUDENTS BY CARPI,
TEACHER IN ORDINARY
OF PUBLIC SURGERY
IN THE BOUNTIFUL
UNIVERSITY OF
BOLOGNA

VENICE 1535

Anatomia Carpi.

ISAGOGE BREVES

Perlucide ac uberime, in Anatomiam hu/
mani corporis, a, cōmuni Medicorum
Academia, ufitatam, a, Carpo in Al/
mo Bononienfi Gymnafio Ordi
ariam Chirurgiæ publicæ
Docente, ad fuorum
Scholafticorum
preces in lucē
date.

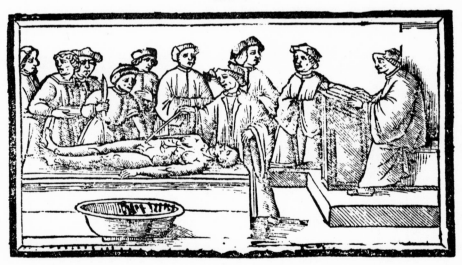

VENETIIS ANNO .D. M.CCCCC.XXXV.

To the Most Renowned and Noble Lord
ALBERTO PIO, Count and Most Meritorious
Master of Carpi, Jacopo Berengarius of Carpi
Sends His Best Greetings

S INCE, Illustrious Prince, we customarily regard those pursuits to which
we dedicate ourselves in our youth as permanent and almost eternal, I
am certain that you cannot have forgotten the many honorable studies we
shared as we learned the rudiments of the gentler Muses under our Roman
teacher, Aldus Manutius, of happy memory. First of all, I doubt that your
lofty and god-like mind has forgotten what youths always enjoy, learning
something as a sport. We both enjoyed it when we had to dissect a pig. The
task fell to me, since I had practiced the surgeon's art under my father's direction ever since childhood. From that time onward I was so fond of anatomy
that I spent all my time at it, not only because of the benefits to be derived
from listening to good professors but on account of the sheer pleasure this
study gave me. There are many books which discuss anatomy, but they are
not well arranged for the reader's comfort. The authors seem to have borrowed fables from other volumes instead of writing genuine anatomy. For
this reason there are few or none at all who now understand the purpose of
this necessary and important art. In addition to the ignorance of anatomy, in
my opinion, the dissection and handling of the members are vile and repul-
sive to many. After I had dissected hundreds of cadavers, I understood why
few physicians of our time comprehended this art. Therefore, wishing to be
of service to the present and to the future world, I thought it wise to write
commentaries on the *Anatomy of Mundinus*. These commentaries serve as a
guide to what the ancient philosophers and physicians have so admirably
written concerning the human body. It is these writings transmitted by many
learned students of medicine that I have been requested to bring to light.
Diligently and faithfully, Academicians ought to desire a knowledge of
anatomy. The art is presented in these commentaries in such fashion that it
can be readily learned. I have composed for the common use of all good men
the present simple handbook on anatomy. It is more complete than any
other. It represents our present state of knowledge; its use will save the
reader long hours of study. I have dedicated the book to you, noble and wise
Prince Albert, following the example of those who have dedicated the fruit

of their labors to one of the gods, so that these labors might, under such auspices, reach men with more certainty. I have done this with enthusiasm, since you are outstanding among the leaders of Christendom, not only in material goods but also in wisdom. Natural and moral philosophy, theology which contemplates God, and the rest of the sciences are combined within you so happily that you will always merit the name of a wise man among men. And since you have always been kind to my birthplace of Carpi and to me, may you continue to be, meritorious Prince. I am not unmindful that I owe fortune, talent, thought, and all my mentality to your generosity, since in your palace, the seat of all learning, I began my study of this most valuable art. Receive, therefore, glorious Prince, with a glad heart and a serene brow this handbook of anatomy so that it may be blessed by your faithful and sincere acceptance. It is no less kingly to accept with joyful countenance gifts that are offered than it is to bestow the most precious of gifts. If indeed offerings of milk from the Cretan shepherd were pleasant to Jove, so also are sacrifices from those who, having no incense, use coarsely ground grains of spelt. The physicians of our age will be indebted to you for the pleasure and usefulness they receive from this little book, than which no other on this subject was ever shorter or clearer. Furthermore, they will always be obliged to sing your praises, as I do. May the Lord bring your desires to fruition. Farewell.

THE SHORT ANATOMY

OF CARPI · Introduction to the Anatomy

of the Human Body by Jacopo Carpi

Illuminate me, Lord, with the spirit of Truth,
and I shall make manifest the works of Thy hands.

THIS book has two parts: the first treats universals, the second, particulars. The first part shows that according to some this name "anatomy" is derived from the Greek *ana-,* which in Latin means "upward from below," i.e., "straight," and *-tomos,* which means "division" or "section"; in other words, straight through the parts, or a division around the parts, of the body.

But a more accurate interpretation of *ana-* signifies in addition to other things investigation of the separate parts of the body. Thus in the composition of the word, "temno," i.e., "incido," signifies "I cut" into the separate parts to discover what and how many they are. Whatever the reason for using the word in connection with things which have parts, the custom of using it concerning animals and especially concerning man has prevailed.

Anatomy, or, in Greek, anatome, is therefore the dividing of all the parts of the living body to investigate their substance, size, number, shape, location, and junctures; also these same properties in dead bodies (to which can be added their innate complexion or organization). Thus Galen said in his book *On the Establishment of the Medical Art:* "I think it is necessary when we take up this art to become acquainted not only with the specific parts and the way they are put together but also with their operation; and in this matter physicians differ from builders. For the latter know only the specific parts of houses and the way they are put together. No part of a house, however, operates, because it is not endowed with life. Physicians, on the other hand, must search out the operations of the members of man, since he is endowed with life and since movements, (innate) bodily habits [*complexiones*], (and influences), and passions exist in living man and not in the dead. Hence these three properties in addition to the six mentioned above are investigated. Thus in real anatomy all nine properties set down here must be considered."*

* [Carpi's quotations are documented in the Translator's Notes, which are listed by page number, and Dr. Roofe's Anatomical Notes are indicated by superior figures in the text.—TRANS.]

But we must begin with the body as a whole, i.e., from the whole, as from something that is better known; first, from a cadaver laid supine in a place suitable for cutting and displaying. Before this, the cadaver must be washed, its hair shaven, and well cleansed of dirt from head to feet. You should know that the body is to be divided into four parts: that is, into three prominent cavities and the extremities, that is, hands and feet along with certain other things.

The first part is the head; this is called caput because the senses take [*capiunt*] their beginning from it. The animal [i.e., spiritual] members are contained in the head; this part is called the highest cavity.

The second part is the cavity between the ribs and the bones connected with them; here the respiratory members and vital organs and some others are located. This is the chest and the "hollow" [i.e., *cassus,* thoracic cage]; it is called the middle cavity.

The third part is the cavity which lies within the abdomen and the portion of the back below the transverse septum, otherwise known as the diaphragm; it descends in front to the pubic bone and in back to the anus. Here the members of nutrition and of generation are partially contained; this is called the lower cavity [i.e., the cavity of the natural members].

The fourth part comprises all the rest of the body: the neck, hands, and feet and the parts serving these.

So much for the first portion.

I. CONCERNING THE ANATOMY
OF THE LOWER CAVITY

THE universal aspect having been viewed, I turn to the special, in which the dissector must begin dissection from the lower body cavity. Here are many members which must first be excised and cast aside lest they hinder the examination of the rest of the body with their decomposition and odor.

Let us say then that this cavity ought to be considered in close connection with those nine previously mentioned conditions or properties. First as to substance. This is different both according to the parts which contain matter and those which are contained. The substance of the parts contained will appear in its proper place. Of the parts in the anterior portion and the lateral portion which contain matter, the substance is like cloth and muscular so that it may be fit for contraction and dilatation for the sake of impregnation and nutriment and other functions similar to these. (It is also venous and arterious.)*

When these parts are in a fleshy body, there is a noticeable fatness. In a lean body there is little fat and sometimes none. Fatness is not properly a member [i.e., adipose tissue is not unique to any organ or structure]; it comes and goes like something superfluous but nevertheless useful.

The posterior substance of this cavity [the posterior wall of the abdominal cavity] is fleshy, muscular, bony, and slightly membranous. (It is likewise venous and arterious.)

The size and form of this cavity are clear. Its site and location lie below the cavity of the vital organs [of the thorax] with the transverse septum between. Beginning from the fork of the inferior part of the chest [i.e., from the breastbone] and from the confines on both sides of the five lower ribs, it passes to the part where the body divides into two extremities [the thighs, legs, and feet from the groin downward]. Its connection with the brain is made by means of the nerves,[1] with the heart by means of arteries,[2] and with the middle cavity by means of some muscles.[3] Its connection with the liver and the members of generation is well known to all.

The lower cavity is a unity. The number of its parts, however, is diverse because some parts "are contained" and others "contain." Those which "con-

* [As indicated previously, parentheses inclose material from the 1523 edition, and brackets inclose my interpolations.—TRANS.]

tain" are the liver [*iecur*] with its little pouch [gall bladder] containing bile; the spleen; the belly, called by many the stomach, although inaccurately; the six intestines with veins scattered among them;[4] the kidneys with their arteries and veins;[5] the bladder with its urethral ducts [ureters] which are called the drains [milkers] of the kidneys; the mesentereon [mesentery] with its glands [lymph nodes]; the portal vein and the vein of the chyle descending with the artery of the aorta;[6] the umbilical veins and arteries;[7] the seminal vessels with the twins [didymi] and the testes; and the uterus in woman.[8] Although the twins and the testes with their scrotum or oscheum are external, they are nevertheless placed in this cavity because they are immediately attached to it.

Of the parts which contain, some are "common," others "proper," and others "more proper." Common are all those parts which surround this cavity, that is, the anterior, lateral, and posterior. The anterior and lateral parts in Latin are called sumen; in antiquity it was called abdomen, in Greek epigastrion, and by some hetron, and in Arabic mirach. The posteriors are called imum dorsi, the lowest part of the back.

Of the "proper" parts, some are in front, others on the sides, and others behind. Those in front are commonly reckoned as five by recent physicians.

The first part, beginning from above in the middle of the body around the lower fork of the chest, is called the sword-and-shield cartilage and also pomegranate. This part is common to the middle and lower cavities, occupying little space.

The second part, immediately under this, is called stomachal because the stomach, that is, the belly, is in this region with its anterior portion; this part extends (almost) up to the umbilicus.

The third is called the umbilical part and is that part in which the umbilicus, closed up in the middle of the abdomen, is made ineffective for its principal task when the child is born.

The fourth part is called sumen by Mundinus because sumen is an elevated region in the front of the body, a part which is taken [*sumitur*] for the whole. This region stretches from the umbilicus as far as the pubic bone.

The fifth part is the one called the comb, within which is the bone of the pubis, or of the comb. In this region, within the lower body cavity, begins the neck of the bladder in both sexes and of the uterus in woman.

The lateral parts proper on each side are equally divided. Physicians commonly reckon two of them, that is, upper and lower. The upper is called the hypochondrium; the lower is called the ilium or flank. The flanks are also called flasks and hollows. In the right hypochondrium is the liver [*iecur* or *hepar*]. The spleen is in the left hypochondrium. The upper part of the flanks begins from the highest of the hipbones and ends down lower in the farthest part of this body cavity. The lowest part of the flanks is called the groin and the bubo. The hypochondria begin from the farthest of the false ribs and terminate lower down at the flanks. Between the flanks and the hypochondria there appears a certain hollow when a man bends forward, which by some is called colago and by others is called itrum.

The posterior parts are called "proper." Some are in the middle, others at the sides. Those in the middle are called the lower spine and the thread [*filum*] of the lower back.

Some lateral parts are upper and others lower. The upper parts are called the lumbar or renal regions. The lower are called the parts above the buttocks or nates.

Certain parts are more "proper." Some are anterior, others lateral, and others posterior. The anterior and lateral coincide. They are first the outer skin, under which are fat and eight muscles, of which four are oblique,[9] two long, two broad, all dilated and united like a cloth [the fascia]; so in fact it is called by Avicenna. It is called the thin fleshy sheet [*panniculosus carnosus*],[10] nor is here in that place a second fleshy sheet, as moderns think.

Under the muscles is a thin tough membrane. In Greek it is called peritoneon, otherwise peritonion,[11] and in Arabic siphac. All these parts compose the abdomen, or mirach.

The posterior parts also called more "proper" are the skin and sometimes some fat. The muscular flesh on each side of the vertebrae, that is, in front and back, is called lumbar by some. Simple non-muscular flesh [tissue] fills the empty spaces of this part. So also do the renal vertebrae,[12] or alchatim; the three bones of the os sacrum, or the three vertebrae called alhovius in Arabic; and the three caudal vertebrae or alhosos and their cartilages with their panniculi, nerves, veins, and arteries, and the peritoneal panniculus. The anatomy of these parts will be told in their respective places. But now I turn to the anatomy of the abdomen (and first concerning the skin).

CONCERNING THE SKIN OF THE LOWER CAVITY AND THE UMBILICUS

You will consider first the place of the umbilicus, which is called the root of man. On the outer surface of the body toward the uterus it has two veins and very often one,[13] and it has two arteries covered over with a shell of skin which is tied up in the newborn and is cut near the abdomen and consolidated by itself and closed up.[14] The middle part of it thus consolidated is called the acrophalus, and because it is wrinkled it is called "little old woman" [*vetula*] in Latin and grea in Greek. Having considered the aforementioned details, cut the skin according to a cross down the length and breadth of the entire abdomen and strip the skin off, keeping the umbilicus unharmed. You will often see the umbilicus enter the body cavity with one notable vein and two arteries,[15] which in children when they are born are prevented from fulfilling their proper task [i.e., when the umbilical cord is tied off].

There is an ascending vein penetrating the hollow of the liver into the portal vein.

Arteries descend through the inner part of the abdomen almost to the pubic bone,[16] and they cross to the back on the sides of the bladder and are implanted, one on the right, the other on the left, into the artery of the aorta bifurcated around the sacred bone below the kidneys. (These arteries of the aorta are called sempiternal.)

From these vessels the blood and [vital] spirit pass to the liver and to the heart of the infant in the mother's womb. You will see this umbilicus better after the anatomy of the abdomen is accomplished. You will preserve the skin carefully for examination. It is double; the first skin is external. This is a thick superfluity of the members and therefore grows again. The second skin is inside, full of strands of connective tissue, and does not grow back again. Under this or in this in both sexes there are two veins, one on the right, the other on the left, visible with difficulty in the newborn. But in foetuses of three months (or thereabouts) they are very clearly apparent as they ascend to the breasts. Look at these and preserve them for the anatomy of the breasts, especially in woman.

In the entire skin of the body there are slender veins scattered among the fibers. They are so thin and narrow that the blood cannot penetrate through them except as a meager fluid which is called the sweat and serosity of the blood.

CONCERNING THE FAT

Beneath the skin there is always some fat, especially in a body not wasted away through illness, greater in one than in another. Remove this so that the members contained under it may be better seen.

CONCERNING THE MUSCLES OF THE LOWER CAVITY

Beneath the fat of the abdomen there are to be seen eight muscles;[17] of these the first four that occur are named oblique. Of these, two are located at the right and two at the left. These with their tendons cover all this cavity from top to bottom anteriorly and ride above all the others. For in each side of the

---

In this figure you have two oblique descending muscles, one on the right, the other on the left. These are above all the muscles. Their fleshy part appears at the sides and in the middle of the cavity. Above the long muscles are their tendons, that is, one on the right, the other on the left. They have small skins [*pelliculares*] and are broad. They terminate in a line which is in the middle of the cavity, as you see, and these tendons have two small skins, that is, underneath and above [fol. 6r].

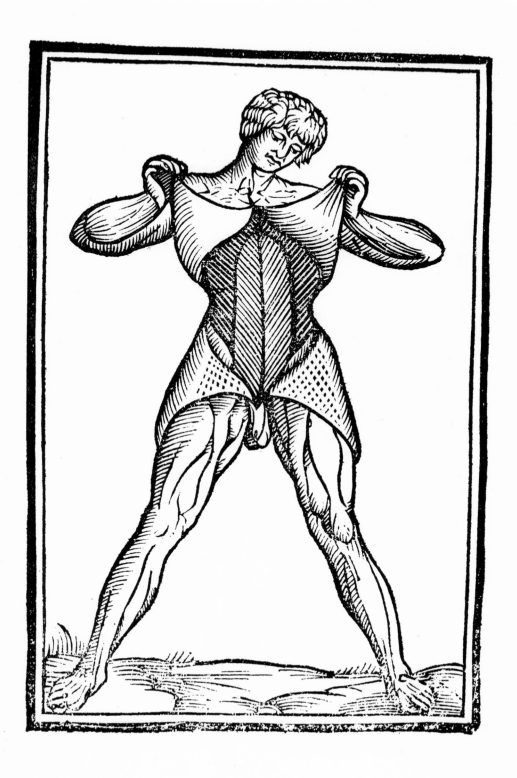

cavity and in front in the middle of the abdomen one of them descends and one ascends. You will see by means of the practiced hand of the leader [i.e., the dissector] that those descending are above those ascending.

You will first carefully separate the descending from the ascending muscles, and you will find that they cross each other on each side of the cavity. One cross is at the right, the other at the left. Their fleshy part crosses itself as does the sinewy or tendinous part. Their thread-shaped projections [villi] stretch always obliquely on the sides toward the middle of the cavity, so that the tendons of those muscles of the right side stretch to the left part of the same right side; and the tendons of the left side stretch in contrary fashion. That is, on each side, tendons of that side cross each other in turn.

The oblique muscles begin to make a tendon when they meet the long muscles, and the tendons of the muscles of the right side and also of the left terminate where the long muscles are contiguous.[18] This place is in the middle of the cavity along a straight line from the pomegranate to the pubic bone.[19]

Descending, they draw their origin from the chest; ascending, they originate from the highest region and the anterior [part] of the hipbones. Their tendons have two tunics [bitunicales]. They are very wide and hard to separate. They arise from the panniculi which cover the muscles and from their sinewy villi dispersed among the muscles.

There are two tunics of the tendons of the muscles which descend on each side,[20] one tunic of the tendons of the ascending muscles. Above, they cover the long muscle of their side from top to bottom. One tunic also of the oblique muscles covers or involves the long muscle of its side toward the lower region, that is, toward the tendon of the broad muscle, because the long muscles lack their own panniculus to cover them, as is apparent to the senses. You can best see the aforementioned oblique muscles in the three immediately following figures. However, look carefully at all their tendons in dissection. Do not move these entirely except those that exist above the long muscles. But the tendons under the long muscles are to be saved until you have dissected those muscles.

In this figure you have two oblique ascending muscles which cross themselves with the two descending muscles placed in the previous figure. These descending muscles are above those ascending muscles. One entire muscle from the aforementioned descending muscles placed above in the previous figure rides with its tendon obliquely above one muscle of those which ascend obliquely, and together they make the figure of the Greek letter χ. The fleshy part of these muscles is at the sides, but their tendons are in the middle of the cavity. They also have two small skins, of which only one rides over the long muscles. The other small skin is below the long muscles. This clings to the latitudinal muscles, and these tendons also terminate in a line[21] which is in the middle of the cavity, as you see [fol. 6v].

CONCERNING THE LONG MUSCLES

There are two long or straight muscles, located in the middle of the abdomen underneath and above the tendons mentioned previously, stretching with their fibers from the lower fork of the chest the length of the cavity to the pubic bone. For this reason they are called long muscles. They are close to each other, occupying the anterior part of the cavity through its width. The width in all is eight fingers or thereabouts. These muscles do not have their own panniculus as the others do. They have, moreover, short tendons ending in the pubic bone, and they have no other tendons. Their substance is fleshy and divided in their width (more toward the skin than toward the siphac) by two sinewy or ligamentous intermedia. One of these is above the umbilical region, the other below, in such a way that each muscle seems to be divided into three noticeably distinct fleshy parts, as you can see in the [fourth] figure following. (And these intermedia mentioned above are ordained by nature because in proportion as the fibers of the muscles are shorter, so much more easily and better do they serve voluntary motions.)

CONCERNING THE BROAD MUSCLES

Having viewed the foregoing parts, cast aside both oblique and straight muscles so that you may see the broad ones better. These are under the long muscles with their tendons, with one of the tunics of the tendons of the obliquely descending muscles as a medial connection. Look at this tunic with care after the long muscles are removed. This tunic is very thin, noticeably bound to the tendons of the latitudinal muscles. These broad muscles have their fleshy part under the fleshy part of the oblique muscles. They are called broad because the position of their fibers is through the breadth of the cavity. They are more above the umbilical region than below it because their principal operation is from the upper region to the lower: this operation is to assist the expulsive force of the intestines. Their fleshy part is toward the back. They terminate in the tendons in that region where the longitudinal muscles are located, and the right one meets the left one by mediation of its tendon. Their fleshy part is under the flesh of the oblique muscles, and their tendons are immediately under the tendons of the aforesaid oblique and ascending muscles. These tendons are also very wide and have two tunics, hard, compacted mutually; they are bound with their panniculus to the peri-

---

In this figure you see how the long muscles are elevated. Under them is a small skin from the tendon of the oblique muscles. This has oblique villi. There is one small skin under each long muscle, as you see in this figure. The long muscles are those which hang between the coxes so that they may appear lifted away from their natural position; thus the tendons of the aforementioned oblique ascending muscles may be seen [fol. 7r].

toneum or siphac. Their tendons cross themselves with the long muscles at right angles.

From what has been said, the location of the muscles of the lower cavity becomes apparent, as well as their substance and size. Their form is conspicuous. They are eight in number, four oblique, two long, and two broad. Their connection has been shown. They are firmly bound up with each other and are united in such a way that they are judged to be one panniculus which is called carnosus [fleshy]. Their habit [complexion] in the living body is clear from their substance.

Their services are to warm the intestines and to maintain united all the members of nutrition and to assist in retention, although they principally assist expulsion. Sometimes they help the members of breathing, especially in breathing in a sudden attack [ictus] and in violent expiration. They can suffer pains of all kinds.

You will see the aforementioned muscles in the first figure following. In the second figure that follows you will see their site, the location and form of the eight muscles of the abdomen, or of the epigastrion or mirach. He who intends to scrutinize these muscles and many other things better, however, must have recourse to my *Commentary on Mundinus;* on account of this book envy will love me after my death.

CONCERNING THE PERITONEUM, OR SIPHAC

Having viewed the foregoing, lift up with care the tendons of the broad muscles from a membrane annexed to them toward the intestines. It is thin and hard, is called the peritoneum and siphac, and surrounds the entire emptiness of the lower cavity and is near it. Its roundness is not, however, perfect. Its substance is sinewy, hard, and its form has been mentioned.

From this panniculus arise two pockets or sacks (called didymi) in which there are two testes located within the scrotum. These are part of the scrotum itself. Its size is as great as the emptiness of the lower cavity. Its site is clear. It is a single panniculus. It is connected with the broad muscles and with all the members contained in this cavity. All the members of this cavity have their own panniculi enveloping them, arising from this peritoneum. According to Avicenna, this panniculus is connected with the pleura. It is also

---

In this figure you see two long muscles laid bare from the tendons of the oblique muscles. These long muscles are above the tendons of the latitudinal muscles. Each muscle has two sinewy or ligamentous divisions in itself extending through its width, that is, one above the umbilicus and the other underneath as you see. Thus each long muscle seems to be divided into three parts or into three muscles. Nature has done this so that to the extent the villi of the muscles are shorter, so much better and more easily they are contracted [fol. 8r].

connected with the transverse septum and the testes. Its "complexion" is that of the other panniculi.

The services of this panniculus are to bind the members of nutrition and generation to the back, to warm the intestines and to preserve them from rupture. It must also restrain the intestines from issuing forth out of the cavity. The panniculus also assists the transverse septum in expelling the contents of the stomach, the intestines, and the uterus.

The panniculus suffers ills [*passiones*] of all sorts. Its own particular ills are fission and softening. Look elsewhere for the cure of all these, since it is not fitting in a demonstration of anatomy to describe the care of ascites, nor the care of wounds of the abdomen nor of the intestines, nor the method of castration nor of the extraction of stone, nor of other illnesses, as Mundinus did. We shall say something nevertheless about the phlebotomy of the guidez vein and perhaps some other particulars (necessary to physicians, about which authors rarely write).[22]

CONCERNING THE OMENTUM, OR ZIRBUS

The previously mentioned members are now to be cast aside so that the rest of the members may be better seen. First appears the zirbus, or omentum.[23] It is vulgarly called the net because it is a member composed of two very thin sinewy little skins with much fat adhering to them.

This member has many pulsating and quiet veins,[24] which are more evident, however, in a thin body than in a fat one. Its panniculi are discontinuous throughout, except around its circumference. It has the form of a pouch or a sack, for there is a great hollowness among its little skins.

Its substance has been mentioned. Its connection is with the siphac, with the colon, and with the spleen. Its location is toward the front; it is extended from the stomach to the groin. Its size is conspicuous. It is one member alone. Its form has been touched upon. Its complexion is the complexion of the parts which compose it. Its services are to assist digestion and to soften the feces. It can suffer ills of all kinds. It causes rupture in the scrotum,[25] in the umbilicus, in the groin, and elsewhere in the sumen [the lower part of the abdomen] if the peritoneum is broken or made soft.

You have in this figure the two broad muscles above which were the long and the oblique muscles, which are now lifted away from them as you see. The fleshy part of these latitudinal muscles is at the sides. Their sinewy part, that is, their tendons, is in the middle of the cavity and is composed of two little skins, that is, beneath and above. They are bound with their panniculus to the siphac [peritoneum]. These muscles are more in the upper part of this cavity than in the lower, as you see, so that they may better expel below that which is in the intestines [fol. 9r].

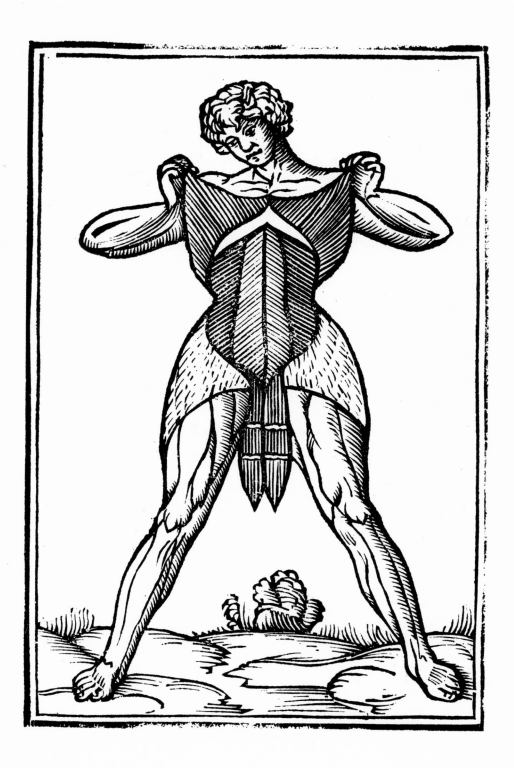

CONCERNING THE INTESTINES

Lift the zirbus, and you will see the intestines. They are continuous from the stomach to the anus. They are wound and rewound so that they may retain the food a long time for the sake of a good purpose. There are six of them.

Ascending first from the lower region is the rectum, a span in length, or thereabouts. The second is the colon, which ascends through the left part up to the region of the kidneys and spleen. Then it crosses over from the left to the right, riding above the stomach. On the right it is united with the sack intestine, which is located around the highest part of the hipbone.

The sack intestine is also called the blind gut [cecum]. It is third in the order of enumeration. These three intestines are said to be gross in substance, for they are fleshy and can be consolidated if they are injured.

The fourth is the long intestine. It is called also the ileum and the revolute or involute intestine because it is wound everywhere through the cavity.

The fifth is the jejunum; the sixth is the duodenum. These latter three are slender and called lactes by some. Their injury is not capable of being healed if it is serious. They are slender above through their connection and thick below. All have two tunics and a common panniculus which arises from the peritoneum. This panniculus covers them over and binds them to the back.

In their inner part there clings the pituita,[26] otherwise known as phlegm, so that it may resist corrosion and lubricate the feces. In them, according to some, are villi of all kinds;[27] many, however, are broad villi. Their complexion is cold and dry. The slender ones are colder than the gross ones because their substance is sinewy.[28] In the gross intestines there is some flesh. Their form is apparent. Their particular location is also apparent and will be apparent from what is to be said. Their services are well known. The intestines suffer ills of every kind.

We must look at the special anatomy of the intestines. First, examine their location with care, and before you separate them from the mesentery, look at their (meseraic) veins, which are called lactes by some.[29] These carry the chyle to the portal vein. In their smallest branches begins the manufacture of the blood under the leadership of the liver. Note also the location of the

---

In this figure are the three forms of the muscles, that is, oblique, long, and broad. You have in the right portion of the figure two muscles which do not cover the entire right part as they do naturally and as demonstrated in the first and second figures. They are thus represented in this place so that their crossing may be better seen. In the left part you have one long muscle and one broad muscle of whose breadth the fleshy part appears. The tendon of the same broad muscle is under the aforementioned long muscle [fol. 9v, misprinted as 10].

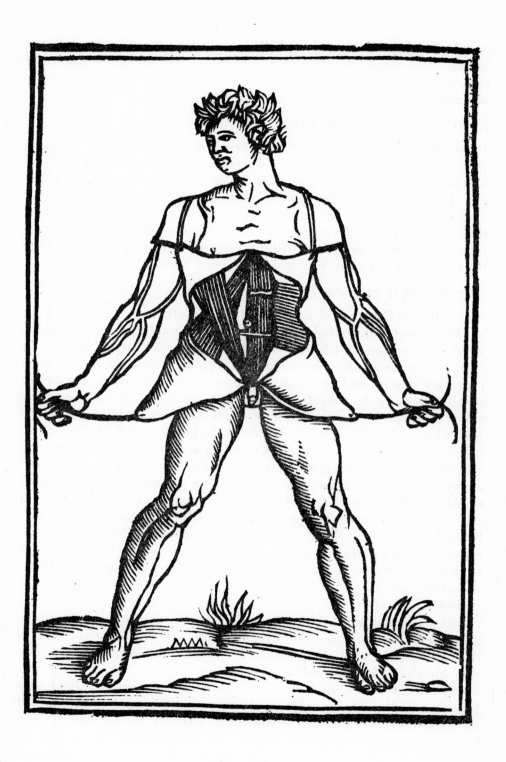

portal vein. This lies beyond the hollow of the liver, stretching toward the intestines and toward the stomach, the omentum, and the spleen with eight branches. Look at all of them carefully if you can before the intestines are cast aside.

CONCERNING THE STRAIGHT INTESTINE

When these are disposed of, you must first look at the rectum or longanon [*longaon*] intestine. This must be cleansed of feces, pressing them by hand into the colon. Its extremity toward the colon must be tied up in two places and the space between the ligatures must be cut. The rectum lies in the space from the anus to the upper regions, ascending about a span through the cavity. It has few meseraic veins because it nourishes its contents very little. It terminates near the left ilium (where the colon begins, united to the rectum). The rectum is united at the point where the colon begins.

CONCERNING THE COLON INTESTINE

You will note that the colon is located on the left. It ascends around the left kidney and is drawn tight there so that it may yield a place to the spleen, which it covers and to which it is attached.[30] It stretches from here to the right side and rides above the stomach, to which it is attached. Hence comes fainting at time of stool; hence arises its pain when food is taken. But kidney pain increases in the second digestion. It is attached to the omentum, by which as well as by the stomach the colon is moistened. It is covered by the lobe [cloak] of the liver in which there is the bile cyst [gall bladder]. This is rather black and bitter. The colon is arched or divided into chambers and abounds in phlegm. Dry, gourdlike masses [*cucurbitini*] and worms [ascaris] are generated in the colon. The feces acquire an unequal shape in it. A rumbling is heard in it before the hour of evacuation [*ascelandi horam*]. It is so situated that, from the upper part to the lower, weighty substance may better descend (and so that it may cover the jejunum and duodenum, guarding them from external [objects], and so that its feces may be pushed back from the omentum which is continuous with the colon, and so that also from the gall bladder the gall or bile may seep back to itself, thus stimulating the expulsion of its feces). Its location is adapted to the administering of an enema and is the proper place for applying medication in colic. Its size is conspicuous. Its substance is sinewy and slightly fleshy. It is fat and solid so that it may resist hard, sharp things. It also has prominent meseraic veins through which the chyle and blood may pass.

Its particular ill is a windy pain. In it are generated stones and hard skins [*coria*] from the dried-up phlegm. Having seen these parts, you can tear the colon from the mesentery to which it is attached and put back the rectum in its place until you take up the anatomy of the anus. The latter can be seen perfectly only when you take up the anatomy of the penis and of the bladder.

CONCERNING THE SACK INTESTINE

Close to this intestine, near the hipbone below the kidney on the right side, is located the intestine called cecus, saccus, and monoculus because it hangs like a sack and has one orifice through which it draws and expels the feces. At different hours, however, it draws from the ileum and expels to the colon. In this intestine is carried on a greater share of digestion than in any other intestine. For it is another stomach. First it attracts, then digests, and afterward expels to the colon.

It is about a span in length. It is as broad as the colon and even more. It is not attached to the mesentery but hangs in the cavity. In the sack intestine worms called serpents are generated.

This intestine, however, is often found rendered inoperative in nature because it does none of the previously mentioned services. Furthermore, it is found also attached to the colon and to the ileum and is, as it were, a sort of addition. Its form appears compactly pressed together. Inside, it is hollow and is less than a little finger in breadth; it is three inches, or nearly that, in length.

CONCERNING THE ILEUM INTESTINE

To this sack intestine as it ascends there is immediately attached the first of the slender intestines, called ileum, long, revolute, or involute. Its substance is slender, its form oblong and round. It is longer than all the other intestines together. In this intestine are more meseraics [blood vessels] than in any other, because of its length. Its location is closer to the ilia; it is situated, however, elsewhere through the cavity. It is attached to the mesentery, from which it must be torn away so that you can well see the other intestines above. Its particular ill is iliac disposition and an ill called "Have mercy on me!" in which the feces pass across to its mouth. (This is discerned from the vomit of the patient.)

CONCERNING THE JEJUNUM INTESTINE

To this ileum is joined the second of the slender intestines. It is called jejunum, hira, hilla, sterile, or empty. It is empty because it is near to the liver, which empties the jejunum by drawing the chyle from it and expelling the contents of the jejunum by means of the bile from the cyst that enters the jejunum near the duodenum. It has more meseraics than any other intestine equal to it in length, so that these meseraics may quickly give aid to the liver. It is, however, emptier in its upper part near the duodenum and is not completely straight but begins to turn around at the point where it is attached to the ileum. There the jejunum is partly covered, partly enveloped. Its color is yellow where it lies near the liver. It is similar to the ileum in substance and form. Its size is conspicuous but not great, and its location lies near the region of the liver and a very little below the liver in the middle of the cavity.

Having looked at these parts you can tear this intestine away from the mesentery also, just like the others, so that you may better see the duodenum, which you will recognize in its length below from the stomach. It is in size as much as twelve fingers in breadth from the stomach toward the lower region.

CONCERNING THE DUODENUM INTESTINE

Last to be seen is the highest of the slender intestines, called duodenum and dodedactilon. Its length has appeared above, and its width is less than that of every other intestine. It is as large as the gate of the lower stomach, called in Greek pyleron, in Latin janitor.

Its substance is slender; it is not turned back but is straight. It is attached to the stomach toward its upper part and is attached to the mesentery. Near the jejunum it is also attached to the bile cyst by a canal which carries the bile to clean out the intestines of phlegm principally and of the feces.

This canal passes diagonally in this intestine between tunic and tunic, so that the bile and perhaps the chyle may not re-ascend to the cyst.

Examine this canal with care and keep it for the anatomy of the aforementioned cyst. Its services are to receive the digested food from the stomach and to transmit it to the other intestines. It suffers all manner of ill.

CONCERNING THE MESENTERY

Having examined these items, cut into the duodenum below the duct which comes to it from the bile cyst, first binding it so that the contents of the stomach may not come out. Cast aside the other intestines if you have first torn them carefully away as mentioned before from the mesentery, or eucharus, which by some is also called lactes. This member is located among the intestines themselves, binding them to the back in their midst. It is composed (in part) of doubled little skins and of fat and glands. In it there are many veins coming from the liver (by way of the portal vein). These are commonly called meseraics; by Galen they are called the hands of the liver because they snatch from the intestines the material of the blood and give it to the liver. These veins are from (some) branches of the portal vein (which are outside the liver). In this member there are also some arteries.

This member is bipartite. The first part is in the upper region attached to the jejunum and duodenum; this part is highly glandulous and has its simple little skins. Through this part the portal veins pass to the stomach, to the spleen, and to the omentum. This part in a pig is of a savory taste and is vulgarly called sweet morsel [*dolce morso*] and sweetbreads [*brisaro, bocca saporita*]. In these large glands there is sometimes contained a material which causes an illness known as melancholia mirachia.

The other part of this member is attached to the other intestines. Its little skins are double because they bind large members to the back. This second part is considered by all as the true mesentery. These two members are nourished by the portal veins.

Their size and form are apparent. The first part is smaller than the second. Their complexion is cold. They are joined to the back by means of the siphac.

Their services are to bind the intestines to the back and to sustain the meseraic veins, the other portal veins, and to moisten the feces of the intestines.

They are also reckoned as two members by the common people. They can suffer all manner of ill. This member or members must be put back in its place until the anatomy of the portal veins has been examined.

CONCERNING THE BELLY, WHICH IS COMMONLY CALLED THE STOMACH

Having disposed of the mesentery, through the duodenum left above inflate the stomach as much as you can. Because of its size it has to be examined last. Then bring it back to a medium inflation so that the things to be sought for in it may be better seen.

First, with the extremities removed, you will note its place, in the middle of the whole [body] immediately under the transverse septum. At the right it has the liver, at the left the spleen, beneath itself the colon and the other intestines. In front are the omentum and the abdomen. Behind is the back, in which it is contained. Its position is oblique, under the diaphragm, attached to the back. The upper part of it is at the left so that it may yield to the liver located on the right and high up so that to its mouth the black bile may more easily pass from the spleen. Its lower part is on the right so that it may yield to the colon, which occupies a large space on the left. Its lower part is on the right toward the lesser pylorus which is on the left toward the colon, since on the right the liver occupies a larger place than the colon located on the left. Its lower part is on the right in such a way that its orifices are not direct and so that it may better retain the food and that the yellow bile from the cyst may more easily enter the duodenum continuous with its lower part.

Its substance is predominantly sinewy. Its color is evident. Its form is round and arched like a Moorish gourd. Its size is evident.

It is connected to the heart by arteries, to the liver and spleen by veins, to the brain by descending nerves. It is attached to the anus by intestines and to the mouth by means of the gullet. It is attached to the zirbus [omentum] toward the front. It has two true tunics, the inner one more sinewy on account of the appetite, more gross, wrinkled, and hard so that it may meet hard foods. This tunic is harder in the upper part and more capable of sensation. The outer tunic is thinner, declining to the nature of small flesh. The inner tunic is in some manner nourished (or gratified) by the chyle. The outer tunic is nourished by the portal vein. The inner tunic has long villi toward the interior, serving for attraction. Toward the outside it has oblique villi that retain; the outer tunic has broad villi that expel.

The fundus of the stomach serves digestion by means of the exterior tunic and by means of the heat of the surrounding members. However, its own proper hidden virtue is for digestion, as that of the uterus is for generation and that of the liver for making blood. Its upper part serves the appetite with the assistance of the black bile from the spleen milking to its mouth, and because of this it is often found black.

The stomach also has a common tunic enveloping itself and binding it to the back; it arises from the peritoneum and is larger than any other member contained in the lower cavity except the mesentery, in which it is doubled. It is so large in the stomach because of the extension of the food.

Its body is attached to the back by its upper orifice, that is, between the twelfth and thirteenth dorsal vertebrae.[31] This orifice is properly called the stomach, and there medicines are placed for the strengthening of the appetite. This orifice is in the extreme lower part of the gullet, or meri [in Arabic]. Perforating the diaphragm in its ascent, it joins the end of the mouth especially with its inner tunic. This orifice is closed by a diaphragm lest through the bending of the body the food should remain behind [fall back]. It is also attached to the back with its lower part, that is, with the pylurus [pylorus], or pyloron or portanarius, in the place where the duodenum is attached to the back by the mesentery. The rest of it is loose and is moved easily everywhere. The portanarius is higher than the fundus which contains the food so that the food may not easily descend into the portanarius (undigested).

It is a single member. Its complexion in any part of its components is cold and dry. Its services are to show appetite, to retain and digest the food, and to give the gross part to the intestines and the benign and digested part to the other members by means of the liver.

It suffers ills of all kinds, and because of its great sensitivity the heart and the brain suffer with it.

CONCERNING THE SPLEEN

Leaving the stomach in its place, instead of examining the portal veins time must be taken for the anatomy of the spleen, or lien. You will first see it located in the left hypochondrium, clinging along its small hollow to the stomach and along the humped portion contiguous to the ribs toward the back and sides, covered by the peritoneum.

You will raise the cadaver, and, when it is in sitting position, you may better see the location of the spleen under the diaphragm immediately in the hypochondrium, as in a living body. But in a dead body as it lies, the spleen is seen under the ribs because its weight drives the diaphragm readily to the upper region, the lung easily yielding, since it is empty and of a loose texture. You can also lift some false ribs so that you may better see the location of the spleen. You will do the same in the anatomy of the liver because of the aforementioned cause. This method would be fitting more or less in demonstrating the location of the stomach which also, because of flaccidity of the lung as the cadaver lies, seems to exist with some of its upper part under the bones of the chest; and this is more natural in a living body.

Its form is a somewhat lunate square. It is of loose, thin substance. It is attached to the heart by large arteries,[32] which you must see, that rarefy the blood. When the blood is rarefied, it nourishes the spleen. It is attached to the kidney by a branch of the portal vein,[33] to the brain by nerves, to the mesentery and omentum by veins, to the siphac [peritoneum] by a covering panniculus, and to the stomach by many veins. Some of these nourish the left part of the stomach, and one of them milks the black bile to the stomach's mouth. Its size is well known. Its complexion is set down as warm and humid, but on account of its content it is regarded as opposite [i.e., cold and dry]. It is a single member. It helps the entire body by purging the bloody mass from the feces, and therefore it provokes laughter [risus, a grinning expression]. From time to time it makes blood, stirs the appetite, aids the digestion of the stomach, and suffers all manner of illness. In it there is sometimes a peculiar running and impediment of strong movement. It is said that when it has been removed by a wound, animals sometimes live. There are those who think that laughter is removed by its magnitude, and sometimes it has changed places with the liver: but this is an unnatural case.

CONCERNING THE LIVER

When you have viewed the foregoing parts, lift up the cadaver as explained above so that the liver may be revealed. This organ is immediately below the diaphragm in the right hypochondrium. It is large in man because he is a warm and humid animal. It is crescent-shaped, hollow toward the stomach, and humped close to the ribs toward the diaphragm above and toward the sides and the back.

Its substance is the flesh of itself and a net of veins scattered through its texture. Its flesh is coagulated blood. It has five lobes, sometimes four and three, sometimes two.

In its hollow is a vein called portal. It enters the liver with five branches scattered throughout the whole liver to its slightest portion toward the humped part. As the chyle is divided among the branches to the slightest portion of the liver, it is better transmuted into blood.

In the hollow there is a small cyst which with ease eliminates from the blood the yellow bile before it can pass to the humped portion. In the hollow also, the umbilical vein enters the portal vein in order to nourish the foetus in the uterus of the mother.

In the humped portion there is one vein called chilis,[34] also with five branches dispersed throughout the entire liver to its slightest portion. The smallest branches of the chilis vein are joined with the same mouths or united with branches of the portal vein and from them suck out the blood when it is purified of yellow and black bile, the blood still mixed, however, with wateriness. The blood acquires its final decoction in the humped portion of the liver.

The liver is relieved of secretions [eventatur] in its humped part by the transverse septum and the chilis vein ascending through the liver to the heart; by this vein the liver is attached to the heart. It also has little arteries in its hollow,[35] by which it is relieved of secretions. These arteries come from the aorta near there and are visible with difficulty. The liver is attached to the space between the shoulders [metaphrenon] by its own panniculus hanging down, to the abdomen by the umbilical vein,[36] and to the brain by a nerve. By means of a panniculus[37] that rises from the peritoneum, by which it is enveloped round about, it is attached also to all members that have a vein. Its complexion is warm and humid. It is a single member. Its parts are its own flesh, the portal vein, the chilis vein, arteries, and a nerve with a panniculus and the cyst of the yellow bile. Its operation is blood-making. Its special ill is dropsy; however, it suffers all kinds of illness.

CONCERNING THE PORTAL VEIN

Beyond the substance of the liver is also the portal vein. According to the testimony of Galen, it was named by a man of intelligence with regard to nature; from him was derived the name which Hippocrates and the entire company of Asclepiades praised, so that it has remained until now. Its branches carry the food prepared beforehand in the stomach to the place of digestion in every animal, which we call the liver.

This vein beyond the liver has eight parts.[38] Two are small, six larger. One of the smaller has two branches: one nourishes the duodenum, and the other nourishes the mesentery contiguous to the duodenum.

The other smaller vein nourishes the stomach near the portanarius.

The first of the six larger parts nourishes the broad exterior portion of the stomach.

The second with some branches goes toward the spleen, from which first one branch goes to the mesentery to nourish it. Then another large branch goes to the spleen; this divides on the way into many branches: of these one large branch nourishes the left lower portion of the stomach.

This branch follows,[39] entering the spleen, and sends forth from itself two branches, of which one ascends and the other descends. There are three parts of the ascending one. One part nourishes the spleen, another nourishes the upper part of the stomach, the third part crosses to its mouth, milking the black pontic bile to incite the appetite, so that most of the bile passes out with the feces through the intestines.

The aforementioned descending vein is bipartite. One branch nourishes the spleen, the other goes to the left part of the omentum and nourishes it.

The third branch of the afore-mentioned six goes to the left to suck the rectum intestine.[40]

The fourth branch of the six larger parts spreads branches among the capillaries.[41] Some of these go to the right portion of the stomach to nourish that, and some go to nourish the right portion of the omentum.

The fifth branch goes to the mesentery in the place where it is attached to the colon.[42]

The sixth goes to the mesentery in the place where it is attached to the jejunum and the ileum with its branches which are called meseraic veins;[43] and this is quite large. The substance of these veins is the same as that of the others. Its size and chief number, site, form, and connections are clear. Its complexion is cold and dry, but by reason of its contents it is warm and humid. Its service is to carry the previously prepared food to the liver. It also begins the second digestion with its branches. It brings nourishment to the stomach, spleen, and omentum, as well as to the intestines. It suffers ills of all kinds, especially constipation and also openings of its meseraics and sometimes tearings [fission]. It suffers with the liver in all its ills.

CONCERNING THE CYST CONTAINING THE GALL OR BILE, WHICH IS CALLED THE GALL BLADDER

The cyst of the bile or gall is called the gall bladder. It is a small bag or sack in the hollow of the liver, adhering to the latter at its middle lobe. It is composed of pannicular substance, thin, solid, lacking blood, with one tunic only, covered by the panniculus covering the liver. In it are villi of all kinds: in its interior it has long and oblique villi; on its outer part it has broad villi.

Its substance is slender because it does not digest anything and hard so that it may resist the sharpness of the gall. It has one duct called common which enters the sack directly; this duct is larger than others. According to some this duct is tripartite (according to others, quadripartite).

One goes to the liver and is joined to the portal vein, by which it draws the gall through narrow passages. In this duct there are only long villi.

Another duct goes toward the intestines. This is twofold for a certain distance. One part of this duct goes to the duodenum in the direction of the jejunum to cleanse the intestines of phlegm and feces by reason of the sharpness of the gall transmitted by it. In the duodenum this duct passes diagonally between its tunics so that the gall contained in the intestine may not turn back and constipate it.

The other duct according to some goes to the pylorus of the stomach to aid digestion with its gall. If this duct is large, it makes a man unhappy because of its continuous emission of gall. Some deny the existence of this duct. Through a common neck (which by some is regarded as the fourth branch), attraction and expulsion are made.

Its size and form are evident. It is a single member. It is attached to the heart by a small artery which it has and to the brain by a small nerve. Its innate complexion is cold and dry.

Its services are to purge the blood by means of gall and to warm the digestion of the liver and to keep the latter from putrefaction. It also assists the stomach and cleanses it of phlegm. It assists the expulsion of [the contents of] the intestines. Sometimes a man lacks a gall bladder; he is then of infirm health and shorter life.

It suffers ills of all kinds. Its special ill is constipation, by which the king's disease, or icteritia [jaundice] is caused. If there is constipation in the common duct and the body is not purged of bile, then choleric ills of various kinds take place. Moreover, the feces can be tinged with color.

If there is constipation in the colon stretching to the intestines and to the portanarius, then the feces are discolored; also the gall is not purged from the bladder but regurgitates into the liver and causes choleric diseases.

And if constipation sets in, in the neck toward the liver, the feces can be colored for some time and will also cause choleric illnesses of different kinds; but during the constipation the feces will be discolored. Other remarks on this subject have been made in my *Commentary on Mundinus*.

CONCERNING THE GREAT CHILIS VEIN AND AORTA DESCENDING AND EMULGENT

Having viewed the foregoing, cast aside the mesentery, the spleen, and the liver. From the humped part of the latter reserve that part from which immediately issues the great canal of the chilis vein, so that you may see its origin, leaving the deflated stomach in its place so that other parts of it may be seen.

First you will see a large vein that goes forth from the gibbous part of the liver—a vein called parigiba, the chilis vein, the hollow vein, and the mother of veins. From this vein by means of its branches to all parts of the living creature is dispensed the blood; the branches are the receptacles of the blood. This vein is thin, porous, and smooth; it does not have two tunics as the artery of the aorta has, and therefore it cannot contain the blood for a long time, since blood is thick, but it may quickly nourish the members. It is also such as to lack movement. But the artery carries the thin blood which by some is called the vital spirit. This artery continually undergoes systole and diastole; therefore it is hard, thick, and compact so that it may not be broken and is such that it holds for a long time the thin blood contained in it. The blood because of its motion is disposed for solution. The upper part of this vein ascends to the heart and beyond by perforating the diaphragm; it is called chilis as it ascends. Of this we shall speak in its place.

This vein descends, clinging directly to the back, and is called chilis as it descends. A great descending artery accompanies it; this is called the aorta. Examine this carefully together with the vein. The vein, however, is above the artery, and both vein and artery are involved with the peritoneum. In the descent of each of them those branches which go to the fasciae or panniculi of the kidneys are first divided. When they are in the region of the kidneys, both vein and artery send out from themselves a notable branch on the right, another on the left; these branches are continuous with the kidneys or joined to them. These branches are called milkers. For the most part the right branch is higher than the left branch because it must be closer to the kidney in order to cleanse it quickly of the wateriness contained in the chyle. The left branch is lower so that its kidney may yield space to the spleen, which lies lower than the liver. The orifices in this branch are indirect [not straight but slanting], so that the first orifice may draw fluid from organs nearby and the second orifice draw fluid from organs farther away, and also so that their action may not hinder each other.

From this vein likewise and from the great artery under the kidneys many other veins and arteries are separated. These nourish the rectum, bladder, uterus, and the parts near these organs. Similarly, in the region of each vertebra from each vein and artery one branch enters the vertebra and is dispersed in the muscles near it. From the previously described branches very slender branches also pass between each vertebra. These branches bring food to the nape of the neck, to the panniculi, and to the ligaments encircling and binding the vertebrae and the nape of the neck itself, as you will see in their dissection. From the previously described branches some go also to the muscles and to the membrane of the abdomen.

This vein and this artery likewise around the os sacrum below the vertebrae of the kidneys are bifurcated into two equal parts in the form of the Greek letter Λ. Some call these bifurcated arteries sempiternal [see p. 42 above]. Into these arteries there pass two umbilical veins, one on the right, the other on the left. These descend at the sides of the bladder into the bifurcated arteries.

These bifurcated arteries and veins, one at the right, the other at the left descending toward the coxae, are according to some divided on each side into ten parts, of which one,[44] nourishing the lower part of the back, is dispersed through the loins toward the kidneys within and without.

Another part divided into capillary branches nourishes the peritoneum.[45]

One nourishes the deep muscles of the coxae.[46]

One nourishes the muscles of the anus, and from this part arise the hemorrhoidal veins.[47]

One nourishes the neck and mouth of the uterus;[48] from this one [the hypogastric] two branches also go to the bladder: one of these branches goes to the fundus, another to its neck. The branch to the neck of the bladder is small in women but in men is large because of the penis.

Another of the ten parts goes to the region of the pubic bone.[49]

Another goes to the long muscles of the abdomen. The branches of this one in ascending are joined with the veins of the chest descending toward these branches. United with these chest veins they go to the breasts. From this branch in woman notable parts go to the uterus, from which two veins not associated with arteries ascend through the abdomen to the breasts. Through these veins the abdomen is joined to the uterus. Therefore in pregnancy and in the time of retention of menstruation beyond what is natural, the breasts may swell as much as possible.

Another of the ten goes to the uterus in woman; in man it goes to the penis and scrotum.

Another goes to all the muscles of the coxae.

The tenth part also goes to the coxae. It is outstanding and descends through the interior of the coxae. When it is near the knee under the posterior surface, it is divided into three branches. One slants toward the outer part of the shin and goes as far as the little foot. This branch is called the sciatica because in its pain incisions bring comfort to it. Mundinus did not know the origin of this branch. Another of the three aforementioned branches descends through the inner part to the foot: this is called the saphena. The third branch holds the middle position among the branches mentioned. All these brings food to the shin and to the foot. The discussion of these will be made in the anatomy of the large foot.

Note that there are more veins than arteries, according to Galen, *On the Usefulness of the Parts* xvi. 13, 14, and according to the testimony of the senses. The reason is that there are many cold members which by their nature do not require relief of secretions, for which also a little spirit is sufficient. Thus they do not have many arteries. In the hands, feet, brain, upper part of the neck, and in the entire skin there are some veins without arteries.

There is, however, no artery without its vein to accompany it; some of these are especially noteworthy. The veins are both attached by a panniculus arising from the artery and are joined together so that the veins may be strengthened and fortified by the aforementioned panniculus. Thus the artery may keep the vein alive, and the vein may give blood to the artery in its needs, the blood by which the vital spirit is made and the artery itself is nourished. Small arteries are not bound with veins by means of the aforementioned panniculus, although both vein and artery are associates. They are associates, however, so that they may keep alive and nourish the members, according to Galen as cited above.

Both veins and arteries go from nearby places to bring food to their members, with the exception of the veins and arteries of the testes and breasts, which come to these from afar off so that the blood may delay a long time within them. Thus the blood is better digested and more easily converted into good sperm and into milk. There are many arteries and veins imperceptible to the senses, such as those which go to the bones, the skin, and to the extremities of the members.

The site of these veins and arteries, their substance, size, and form are evident. (Often, however, the veins vary in their site, number, and size; thus authorities do not agree about them.) The number of their branches is imperceptible. Their connection is clear from what has been said and is to be said. Their services are to nourish and keep alive the entire body. The ills they suffer are of all kinds.

Compositional diseases occur in them from their great amount of obstructions [constipations], which are worse than the obstructions of the nostrils, intestines, and similar places because their obstruction keeps the members from being nourished, not permitting the blood to flow to them, also because they force the blood to regurgitate to the liver, which brings about constipation in it and induces its decay or some other serious ills. Their constipation is bad because it is often unrecognized and because medicines are applied to them with difficulty, both internally and externally. Their injury can be brought about by intrinsic and extrinsic causes. There are three of these. One is commonly called diabrosis, which is corrosion of the vein, from *dia-*, which is *de*, or "composition," and *-brosis* (or *-rosis*), which is an eating-away. Another is called rexis, which is interpreted as rupture. The third is called anastomosis, which is the same as the opening and dilatation of the veins, whence come the verses

> Diabrosis venas corrodit; rexis easdem
> Scindit; anastomosis eas (has) aperire facit.

[An elegiac distich: "Diabrosis corrodes the veins, rexis splits them, anastomosis causes them to open."]

To the milker veins other ills may occur, such as weakness of the accustomed attraction of the watery blood, just as also to the kidneys. Thus they either do not attract or do so weakly, whence comes difficulty [in voiding urine] or the total voiding of urine, even when there is no urine in the bladder. In this case ignorant physicians make a mistake in trying to extract the urine with a syringe or by some other manual operation from the bladder. This is an unusual case, very often fatal, as I have seen many times. Among other cases, I was in charge along with many honored physicians of the magnificent and illustrious Don Galeazzo of the noble family of Pallavicini, who was choked by a urinal aquosity collected in the veins of his entire body; this aquosity induced quinsy. For this we applied cupping glasses without scarification in order to divert the aquosity. The cupping glasses were filled through the pores of the skin with pure aquosity. I have written this down incidentally for the use of young men.

CONCERNING THE KIDNEYS

With the aforesaid milker branches are joined two solid fleshy bodies covered by the peritoneum. These are called renes or renones [kidneys], for they are two and not one like the gall bladder. Because the aquosity of the body is greater than the feces and the foam of the blood, this aquosity requires one large expurgatory or two small ones. One kidney is smaller so that it may not squeeze and press the intestines or the back. There are two kidneys so that if the operation of one should be injured, the work of the other would continue. They are solid so that they may handle much within a small space, so that blood may not issue forth with the urine through some of their pores, so that they may attract only the thin matter by sucking it, and finally so that they may resist the sharpness of the urine. They are also made solid because a thick body is stronger at drawing something to itself.

Their size is evident; their form is conspicuous. This [form] is similar to that of a kidney bean. Their complexion is warm. They are joined to the brain through nerves by means of the panniculi which surround them, to the liver by the aforementioned veins, and to the heart by large arteries. Galen noted that there are large arteries in the kidneys, not only for the sake of nutrition and the maintenance of life, since the kidneys are small members for which a small artery would be sufficient, but also because they cleanse the heart from aquosity and bile. He also said that often the aorta draws from the stomach and from the intestines the impure blood, or rather the chyle, which the milker arteries purge to the kidneys.

I myself saw in my study at Bologna in the year 1521 at a public anatomy a milker artery that made a pore [or duct] on the right beyond the kidney which at a notable distance below the kidney passed along the urethral duct that arose from the aforesaid kidney, and both ducts went through one canal to the bladder. Nevertheless, this milker artery also entered the kidney in the accustomed place, and in this individual [cadaver] the kidneys were attached to each other as if they were one kidney. This kidney had two veins, two milker arteries, two urethral ducts, and a single panniculus surrounding them. All these organs occupied the accustomed place of the kidneys and also the middle of the back, which is in the space between the spleen and liver a little below them.

Leave the left kidney then in its place until the spermatic vessels are examined. Cut the right kidney in its hollow through the middle, following its longitude up to its center, examining the place of the vein and of the great artery itself,[50] which enter the substance of the kidney in its concave part. By these [the vein and artery] the kidney draws its spirit and nourishment and the aqueous superfluities of the entire body mixed with the bile. All these mingled [fluids] pass through the entire substance of the kidney, although it is solid, because they are thin. The blood alone would not pass to the smallest parts of the kidneys, since they are solid, unless it were mixed with aquosity and bile. All these, when mixed, resembled the washing of flesh from the kidneys drawn by the milkers from the liver and from the heart by the mediation of the chilis vein and the aorta artery.

This blood mixed with much aquosity alone is retained by the kidneys for their nourishment. Water with bile separated from the blood passes to a certain notable vacuity which exists in the center of the kidney, as if to a pool.[51] A channel or canal duct called uritides leads this [water] to the bladder. This duct was called urethra [ureter] by the Greeks. It is an oblong body, supplied with a panniculus, solid, perforated, and originating from the body of the bladder, which it resembles, as they say. It terminates at the kidney. Examine this duct with care and preserve it together with the kidney for the anatomy of the bladder. In the kidney there is not any net or other pannicular sieve, as some think there is, for the kidneys are made as concave organs with orifices, some of which attract while others emit the thin watery superfluity.

Galen said, *On the Usefulness of the Parts* iv. 12, that many drunkards who drink entire jugs full and urinate a proportion of what they drink are not hampered in regard to discretion [voiding of urine]; but very readily and deceptively the blood which comes to the hollow of the kidney is purged entirely by the kidneys without touching the vein. The aforementioned pool [of the kidney] has around itself a solid panniculus perforated by more than ten large foramina by which,[52] through the mediation of a certain small substance of the kidney similar to the nipples of a woman's breasts, nature milks the urine into the aforementioned concavity.

The connection of the kidneys is evident from what has been said. They are also joined by a small nerve to the brain through a panniculus which covers them. Their services are to purge the entire body of superfluous aquosity and bile, but principally the liver and heart. Much aquosity, however, remains in other veins mixed with the blood, which is called the vehicle of nourishment. This appears in phlebotomized blood or in blood extracted by some other method from the body.

They suffer all sorts of illness; almost all are difficult to heal, such as diabetes, that is, an almost continuous dripping of the urine. They suffer also a weakening of their power to attract; with this weakness the urine does not go to the bladder, and in this manner sometimes the living creature is suffocated or perishes in some other way. Ascites [dropsy] is also brought about by such weakness. They also suffer from stones, sand, and hairs, but the hairs are generated or condensed in the urethral ducts. The stones are red and small; they are often created in the aforesaid pool or cavity. When the kidneys are weakened and cannot retain the blood, the urine comes out bloody. It comes out like this also when the liver is weak, not distinguishing the aquosity from the blood with the separation and quantity which it ought to have.

CONCERNING THE SEMINAL VESSELS

Having disposed of these items in each sex, you will first note in the great chilis vein and in the aorta artery, sometimes above, sometimes below the kidneys, a small vein and an artery which, united for some distance,[53] touch each other as they descend to the testicles of the right side.

You will also note two similar vessels descending in the same way and united on the left side, one from the milker vein of the left kidney, the other from the aorta artery. All these small veins and arteries thus descending are called the vessels which prepare the sperm. These members are surrounded by a panniculus originating from the peritoneum, called aegitroides by Celsus. The vein lies above, but the artery lies below.

These vessels are broader and harder in the male than in the female except at times of impregnation and menstruation, as is evident to the senses by the large amount of blood retained in them at those times. But at other times in the male they are harder and broader; they are always also longer because they have to carry their contents a longer distance. They are of such a nature because the male sperm is greater and thicker than that of the woman. By reason of the length of the vessels in the male the sperm is more digested. The sperm of the right side generates males because its material is more digested and cleansed from aquosity. The sperm on the left side, however, generates females because it is cold and watery, coming from the aforesaid milker arteries filled with watery blood.

These vessels in each sex come together in the place from which they arise but separate on their way from it. Their termination in woman is within the body, as will be told in the anatomy of the uterus, which is postponed to the anatomy of the penis and of the anus for the sake of a better order.

These vessels in the male descend on each side to the pubic bone at the end of the ilia above the loins and are therein called also lumbar vessels. These vessels descending above the pubic bone pass on each side within a pannicular covering arisen in part from the ends of the siphac which is commonly called didymus and cremasters. They pass within the scrotum to a point near the testes, as can be seen in one side alone, leaving the other side intact for the examination of the anatomy of the didymi. Take care you do not destroy the scrotum on either side, but draw to the upper region toward the pubic bone that vessel alone which you intend to see together with its didymus and testicle.

These vessels descending to a point near the testes are quite hard and are coiled like dilated veins, whence they are called variciform. When they meet the testes, around which they are entwined so that they may not injure them with their hardness, they are made soft; and therein these vessels are called epididyma and anendor and andros.

From these vessels the material of the sperm passes immediately to the testes. In the substance of the latter the material acquires a white color and the generative force. It is expelled from the testes to the aforesaid soft vessels called epididyma, from which it passes to other vessels lower down and continuous with the epididyma. These are called the vasa deferentia; their substance is white and harder than that of the other vessels. These vasa deferentia in the male ascend from the testes to the pubic bone contiguous with the aforesaid descending vessels which prepare the sperm. These vasa deferentia, having thus ascended in the highest part of the bone of the pubis, on each side within the belly are bent back. Save these vessels carefully together with the testes until you have seen the anatomy of the didymi and of the testes.

These vessels bent back within the belly descend between the rectum and the bladder, and there they dilate into many caverns filled with sperm. Therefore these vessels are called those which conserve and carry away the sperm. Galen, following Eracleus [Herophilus], calls them parastrata [parastata] adeniformia because adenous flesh surrounds them.

On the right and left these vessels perforate the neck of the bladder, and within the penis near the anus they send forth the sperm, which later is expelled through the canal of the penis.

CONCERNING THE DIDYMI

These vessels together with the testicles from the fundus of the scrotum to the lowest part of the ilia on both sides are covered with one panniculus whose larger part arises from the peritoneum, at the end of the abdomen in the descending scrotum. This is commonly called the didymus and suspensory of the testicle; by the Greeks it is called cremaster. Examine its substance, which is made up of three and probably, according to some, of four windings of panniculi.

The first is on the outside and arises from the panniculi of the vertebrae. Another arises from the siphac, or peritoneum, contained near the femur within the abdomen; this is called dartos by Celsus.

From these two one single skin, as it were, is made because of their strong connection.

Another winding from the panniculus immediately covering the aforesaid vessels arises from the peritoneum near the back. This is called aegitroides.

Another is made from the tendons of the muscles of the testicles; this is small.

Examine their size, connection, complexion, and number. They have the form of a cyst, drawn tight in the upper part and broad in the fundus, as broad as the thickness of the testes.

Their services are to lift up the testes and to maintain the aforesaid vessels.

CONCERNING THE SCORTUM (WHICH SOME CALL SCROTUM)

From these panniculi and skin is composed the oscheum, or scrotum, that is, the pocket of the testes, in which there are some nerves which give sensation to it and some arteries and veins which nourish it. (The scortum Celsus calls scrotum.) The scrotum is one member common to both didymi. It is a sinus or chamber for the twin testes and the seminal vessels.

This member is divided through the middle by a thin membrane which is called by some the suture and the taurus and the tendon. This also appears somewhat in the exterior skin in the middle of the scrotum (making a certain wrinkle), following the length of the body. The size, form, site, number, and connection of this member are evident. Its complexion is cold and dry; its services are clear.

This member with its didymi suffers every kind of ill. Its special illness is dilatation by means of which many ruptures called hernia are caused, that is, zirbal, omental, or intestinal. In the scrotum also is caused watery hernia, or hyrnea, windy, humoral, fleshy, and varicose, which is brought about (by repletion of the seminal vessels) by thick or excessive and watery blood.

CONCERNING THE TESTICLES

With the aforesaid suspensory organs on each side are two glandulous white members similar to the flesh of the breasts, which are called testicles. Their form is oval, and therefore they are also called eggs. Their substance lacks blood and all sensation. They feel, however, through their panniculi. Each of these members has two muscles clinging to their panniculi so that they may hold the members and lift them in order that they may not be lax.

Their size, number, and site are evident. Their innate complexion is temperate in action, humid in passivity. Their influence nevertheless is warm. By means of this, according to Aristotle, they draw to themselves like a cupping glass from the entire [body] the material of the sperm. By physicians the testicles are placed among the principal members. They are attached to other principal members by veins, arteries, and panniculi. Their service is to preserve the species. They suffer ills of all kinds.

CONCERNING THE BLADDER

Having examined these items, lift up the kidneys with the urethral ducts that arise from the bladder and pass within the bladder tunic more toward the neck than the fundus, diagonally, so that the urine may not regurgitate to them [the ducts]. Stone created in the kidneys sometimes passes through these ducts to the bladder, making in the ducts an extension accompanied by intense pain because they are sinewy like the bladder.

First cut the body of the bladder around its fundus, which is composed of one tunic. In its exterior part there pass two nerves to provide it with sensation.[54] First note its site, which is in the lower part of the body cavity in the hollow of the aqualiculus [abdomen], in which are also the rectum intestine toward the back and in woman the uterus in their midst.

You will also note its connection, size, form, and number. Its substance is sinewy from sinews of a ligament which cannot be consolidated if it is injured. It is fleshy at the neck and can therefore be consolidated [healed] there. Its neck is united to the penis throughout up to the end of the glans, whence issues the urine.

Its complexion is cold and dry. It is surrounded by one panniculus arisen from the peritoneum. Its function is to retain the urine for a long time so that a man need not arise frequently to void it. But as the urine flows continuously to the bladder from the kidneys, certain glandulous pieces of flesh assist its retention,[55] surrounding and compressing the beginning of the neck of the bladder outside, causing some bendings in the neck itself. Because of these bits of flesh the bladder is not completely emptied of its aquosity. One single muscle of the bladder which surrounds its mouth assists its voluntary retention and expulsion.

The bladder can suffer all kinds of ills which are sometimes incurable, such as very large stone and excoriation in a bilious body or in an old man. (Its severe injury is fatal.)

CONCERNING THE PENIS

After the aforementioned members there appears the penis, which is of ligamentous substance, sinewy and cavernous like a sponge,[56] with, however, some muscles. The penis, like the tongue, has more and larger veins and arteries than any other member similar to it in size. Through the means of the aforesaid porosities at the instigation of the imagination the penis alone is often magnified and erected. For in it there is a natural quality by which, when the living creature is moved to coitus, the penis is inflated and dilated, just as motion is naturally brought about in the heart and in the arteries. In the latter, motion is brought about, however, always by necessity [involuntarily]; in the penis sometimes (and often it is useless) by necessity. Its origin and site are in the middle of the pubis, as is known to all.

Its form is oblong and round. It has in it a canal through which the urine and the sperm go forth. Its highest part is called the glans [acorn] and the head of the penis. There it is compact, hard, and dull to sensation so that it may not be injured in coitus. A certain soft skin surrounds this glans; it is called the prepuce, obedient to reversion [pulling back] at any rubbing.

This prepuce in the lower part in the middle only along its length is attached to the larger part of the glans by a certain pellicular member vulgarly called "the little thread" [*il filello*]. Its number and size are apparent. Its innate complexion through influence is warm and humid. It is attached to the pubic bone with adenous parastasis [by the prostate gland], to the bladder by means of the canal which draws off the urine, to the brain by means of nerves that come to its muscles and skin, to the heart and liver by means of the aforementioned descending arteries and veins.

The penis has three foramina or passageways: a broad one which is common to the sperm and urine, and two small ones through which in common there passes the sperm coming from the aforesaid seminal vessels. These two orifices, or vessels, pass into this canal in the place called the perineum (which in the male is the place between the anus and the root of the penis and in the female is between the anus and the fissure at the neck of the uterus). It is between the penis and the anus. From these foramina to the bladder this canal is called the neck of the bladder. From here up to the end of the glans the foramen is called common since it is the canal of the penis; by some it is called urethra.

The penis has four muscles, two toward its lower part on both sides but [joined into] one near the urinal canal, which are extended along its length. They dilate the penis and elevate it so that the sperm may penetrate it with ease. Two other muscles of the penis arise from its root toward the pubic bone, coming transversely toward the glans in its upper part. When these are stretched the penis is elevated, and when they cease their tension, it is depressed. If tension occurs in one muscle and not in the other, the penis will decline in the direction of the tensed muscle.

The usefulness of the penis is chiefly for the preservation of the species. By means of it the sperm is sent into the field of nature, that is, the uterus. If the penis is of moderate size, like the tongue, it is praised and is useful. When it is short, the penis does not lead the sperm to the place where it ought to go, and its too great length is the cause of harm to the spirits in the sperm.

The penis also by means of its connection voids the bladder of urine. A sign of this is that when a louse is applied to its extreme orifice, the louse's biting provokes the urine.

The function of the prepuce and of the aforementioned little skin which attaches the prepuce to the glans are to furnish some delight in coitus and to guard the glans from external harm. The Hebrews do away with the prepuce in circumcisions, thus operating against the intent of nature. The penis suffers all kinds of ills. Its special ill is priapism.

You must view this anatomy well, having first noted the foregoing items and the site of the rectum intestine. With a knife, hook, steel saw, or other means separate the pubic bone from its lateral part and together with the bone separate a notable part of the nates, that is, the part in which are the muscles of the anus, and lift up the rectum, bladder, and penis with the seminal vessels and urethral ducts aforementioned. Place these members, washed and cleansed from the filth and blood contained in them, upon some table so that you may see them better, putting carefully away the pubic bone alone from the aforesaid members.

First you will notice the place of the urethral ducts, mentioned before, entering the bladder; place in them a probe or rod or something of the sort, and you will see it penetrate this place diagonally through the substance of the body of the bladder in its hollow, as has been said.

Having viewed these items, you will also see the aforementioned seminal vessels passing between the rectum and the bladder; with some cutting instrument carefully separate the rectum from the bladder, since in this place these members are very firmly attached; you will see the aforementioned parastata, cavernous and broad. Cutting into these parastata, you will see the sperm contained therein for two or more coitions. These vessels terminate in the canal of the penis.

Around this place you will see a notable glandulous flesh at the sides of the neck of the bladder which in some way digests and whitens the sperm contained therein, or at least keeps it from drying out, preserving likewise the genital force or spirit within it.

These pieces of flesh also keep the neck of the bladder and the penis from drying out; the penis, hanging outside because of its length, is apt to dry out and close up. For this reason these pieces of flesh are lacking in woman. These pieces of flesh with a certain oiliness in them withstand the sharpness of the urine.

Having noted these items, you may cut the penis longitudinally, and you will see the aforementioned canal with its orifices through which the sperm passes. These are two, one on the right, the other on the left, not far distant from the cavity of the bladder. You will also see the cavernous or porous body of the penis like a sponge which is not very full of holes but somewhat compact.

CONCERNING THE RECTUM   *As*

Having noted the foregoing you must recall the place of the rectum intestine, which you laid aside above for the anatomy of the anus. This you will consider to be in the cavity of the aqualiculus [cavity of the pelvis], and it ends within the buttocks in the place called anus, from which go forth the excrements of the first digestion in the natural order. The highest part of it tends to the left, where it is attached to the colon intestine.

You will also consider its evident size; its form, site, and number you have seen above. It has connections with the heart, the liver, and the brain, and with the bladder in man, with the uterus in woman.

Consider also its complexion, which is cold. For this reason it is within the nates so that it may not be harmed by the cold.

Then cut it down its length, and washing it very carefully you will see its inversion, which ascends from the outer side inward for four fingers or thereabouts. For you will often see the terminus of its inversion, and sometimes you will not see it. This inversion cleanses the rectum of feces, because in defecating the rectum descends somewhat. This is best seen in horses which are defecating.

Its lower extremity is called the anus, podex, and sphincter. It has many other names recited by me in my *Commentary on the Anatomy of Mundinus*.

Its substance is fleshy and panniculous. It is rendered more fleshy with muscles. In it there is some fat on the outside. In it also there are many

---

You have in this figure the uterus with its horns at the sides, below which are the testiculi in their natural place attached to the seminal vessels. These vessels terminate at the body of the uterus, as you see, and they arise above near the region of the kidneys from the milker vein and the chilis vein, as was said previously. This uterus is pictured large as if it were pregnant. In its anterior part is the bladder with its urethral ducts. The neck of the bladder terminates in the neck of the uterus a little above the fissure which is called the vulva. The testicles in this picture are in the place where they belong. These items, however, are better seen in the anatomy of a pregnant woman, although they can also be seen in one that is not pregnant [fol. 21v].

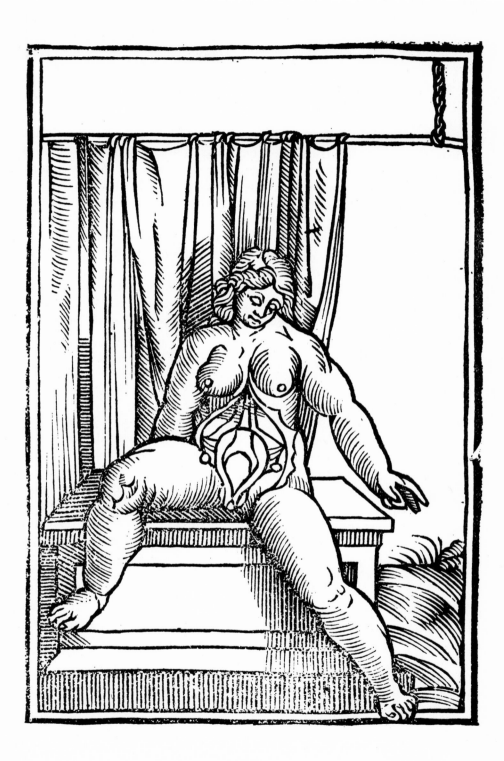

broad, long villi and a few oblique villi. The long villi are outside and inside,[57] aiding the expulsion by drawing it lower down.

In it there are four muscles.[58] One is in its farthest orifice; mingled with skin this muscle is dispersed throughout the anus and constricts it on all sides so that the feces are completely expelled. Another muscle lies more within, elevated toward the head of the man. This muscle has two heads and here is attached with the root of the penis; its use is to compress the end of the anus. After these, there is one equal muscle above the others, stretching transversely; its service is to lift up the rectum; when this is made soft a precipitation of the rectum outside between the nates to a certain distance is caused.

In the extremity of this intestine appear many veins, noticeable in some, hidden in other [cadavers], which are called (mariscae and) hemorrhoidal,[59] flowing in paroxysms. Examine these.

These veins arise from the branches of the descending chilis vein which nourish the muscles of the anus. Many of them are used for looseness [of the bowels] in the service of purgation, nor are they made weak because of this [service].

The function of the anus is to lead forth the feces at the appointed time. Its muscles help the parastata in emitting the sperm in coitus. A sign of this fact is that some of them come together and carry out [the feces]. They also assist the bladder in the voiding of urine.

The anus suffers all kinds of ills, which are hard to heal. Among other ills, the extremity of the rectum, like the uterus, falls forward. We lead it back by means of astringents. Wartlike excrescences [condylomata] also or certain tubercles, fig [hemorrhoidal tumor], and fungi are created in the anus, as well as piles and rhagades, or rhagadiae [fistula, hemorrhoids], which are accustomed to arise from its inflammation. Sometimes a lascivious shamelessness of riotous living and burning lust in either sex by seeking low retreats or byways cause these ills. Neglected nature not without the injury of divine majesty itself brings about these sicknesses.

CONCERNING THE NON-PREGNANT UTERUS

Having examined these members contained in the lower body cavity of man, I pass to the anatomy of woman, in which we are to see the anatomy of the uterus, of its testes with the seminal vessels, and its bladder.

You have in this figure the uterus intact with horns and testicles above the horns. You see how the seminal vessels go to the testicles and from the testicles to the uterus, but the testicles are not in their natural place, for this is below the horns. The testicles are placed thus above the horns in this figure so that the seminal vessels may be better seen passing into the horns. You see also in this figure how the mouth of the uterus is above the neck, because its mouth is that foramen which is seen above the neck of the uterus [fol. 22r].

The uterus, also called vulva, has two parts, that is, a receptacle, or sinus or cavity, and a cervix, or neck. It is a member created by nature for propagation. The substance of its receptacle is sinewy, confusedly mingled with sinews of a ligament and flesh. Therefore it has little sensation. It is composed of one tunic surrounded by the peritoneum, and it is sinewy so that it may be extended in coition and so that it may be enlarged from a small size in childbirth. All of its cavity is moved to the center in the reception of the sperm, which it embraces and touches with its sides.

The substance of its cervix, or neck, is of muscular flesh, like cartilage with some fat; it has wrinkle upon wrinkle which give delight by rubbing in coitus. This part is quite sensitive.

Its cavity is called uterus, venter, and receptacle of the foetus. The fissure in the orifice of the cervix is called the pudendum muliebre and vulva and nature and the genital mouth.

The penis is placed in this cervix in coitions.

Between the cervix and the inner receptacle is a certain substance of pellicular flesh which is quite sensitive, perforated in the middle, capable of dilation and constriction, called the mouth of the uterus and having the form of the head of a mullet, or of a cephalus or tench, or of a newborn kitten. In coition, childbirth, and menstruation this substance is opened in the order of nature. But at other times, especially when pregnant, it is so closed that not even a thin needle can enter it except by force.

The form of the cervix is oblong, round, concave. In the violated woman it is as large as the penis of the man that has coition with her. It is, however, smaller in a virgin.

Around the middle of the cervix is a panniculus (called) virginal, like a net made of thin ligaments and many veins, which a violated woman lacks because it is broken in the first coitus with a male. This panniculus is called eugion, cento, and hymen.

At the end of the cervix little skins are added at the sides; these are called prepuces.

Within the cervix a little toward the pubic bone there passes the short neck of the bladder, whose orifice is closed by certain small fleshy and pan-

---

You have in the lower body cavity of this figure an open uterus in which you see some black dots indicating the heads of the veins which are called cotyledons. Furthermore, you have the uterus inverted outside the body cavity; it is the figure above which you see the index finger of the present human figure. In the fundus of the uterus there is a certain depression, as you see. This depression distinguishes the right sinus from the left, nor is there found in the uterus any other division. Those black dots are cotyledons; you see how the neck of the uterus is without cotyledons and how the neck resembles a penis [fol. 22v].

nicular additions; by means of these and by the prepuces aforementioned with the mediation of the air some noise is made in voiding urine.

The form of the receptacle is quadrangular with some roundness; the lower part is concave like the bladder.

To the receptacle toward the cervix on each side there is a ligamentous addition bound to the back toward the anchae, with the shape of a snail's horn. Therefore these are called the horns of the uterus.

Near these horns on both side is one testicle, harder and smaller than the testicle in man, not perfectly round but compressed like an almond. In them is generated a sperm, not thick as in the male nor warm, but watery, thin, and cold.

These testes do not have one panniculus in which both may be contained, as the scrotum in the male, but each has its own panniculus arisen from the peritoneum which attaches them near the horns of the uterus, and each has one small muscle by which it is moved.

Within these testes are implanted the aforementioned seminal vessels, which, descending from the chilis vein, from the aorta, and from the milker veins, are called the vessels of preparation. Thence other vessels called those which carry away [deportantia], continually dilating themselves, stretch to the receptacle. They lead the sperm into the cavity of the uterus (near its mouth).

The orifices of these vessels are called fossulae and cotyledons.[60] Through them flow the menses. From them the foetus draws nourishment by the umbilical veins and arteries attached to the aforesaid fossulae. In woman there are no parastata vessels nor the vessels of the epididyma, because in woman the vessels are soft and do not harm the testes, as they do in the male because of their hardness.

The entire uterus with its testicles and seminal vessels is similar to the members of generation in men, but the male members are completed outside, since they are thrust out on account of their heat. The members of women are diminished and retained within the body because of their lesser heat.

The uterus is, as it were, a converse [analogous] instrument. For the neck of the uterus is like a penis, and its receptacle with testicles and vessels is like the scrotum. The scrotum has a cavity within itself when turned in,

---

Because a tenfold repetition is wont to please, you have here two other images of the uterus, of which one is inverted. In this you see how throughout in the receptable there are many black dots indicating so many cotyledons, which do not, however, appear in the neck. In the second image you see the natural uterus with testicles and spermatic vessels and ligaments for the horns with which it is attached to the anchae. You also see the neck and mouth through which pass the menses and the foetus and through which the male semen enters [fol. 23r].

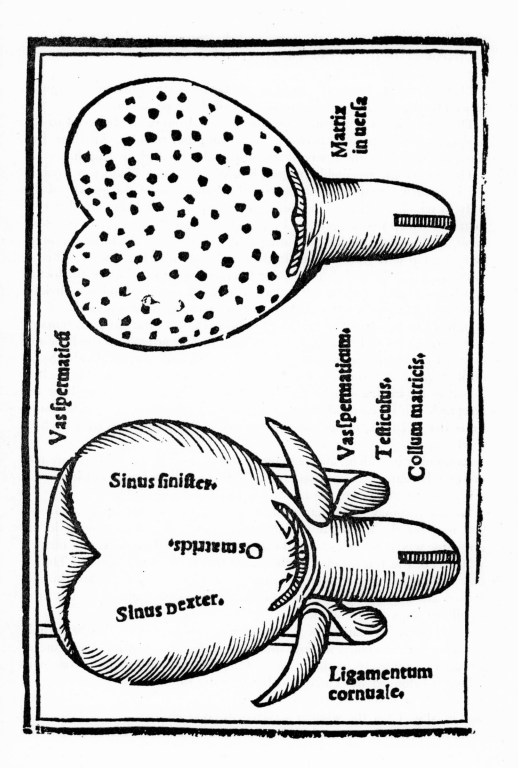

Matrix in uersa

Vas spermaticū

Vas spermaticum.

Testiculus.

Collum matricis.

Sinus sinister.

Os matris.

Sinus dexter.

Ligamentum cornuale.

and when turned outward the testes and the seminal vessels lie outside like the receptacle of the uterus. The testes and vessels of men, however, are larger.

The site of the fissure of the uterus is between the anus and the pubic bone. The place between both orifices is called the perineum.

The cervix ascends upward from the fissure through the belly up to the receptacle, whose place is between the rectum and bladder. All these [organs] are located in the cavity of the aqualiculus through its length.

The size of the receptable in girls is small, and their bladder is smaller, nor is its cavity completed except with the completion of the growth of the body to which it belongs. In adults, unless pregnant, it is not much larger than that which may be grasped by the hand. It grows however in menstruation, having walls which are rather fleshy, dense, and thick. In the pregnant woman it is greatly dilated and appears thin, rather sinewy. Then it ascends toward the umbilicus more or less according to the size of the foetus.

It has a single cavity or cell, which somewhat near its fundus is divided into two parts, as if there were two uteruses terminated at one neck.

In its right part most often males are bound fast, in the left part, females.

It is joined to the brain by nerves, to the heart by arteries, to the liver and breasts by veins, to the rectum intestine by panniculi, to the bladder by its neck; because it is short, it does not penetrate outside as in the male. It is joined to the anchae [hipbones] by the horns, but by the horns above the receptacle it is on each side broken and thus falls forward to the side. Sometimes the receptacle passes completely outside the body by its own neck or cervix.

Its number is evident, and perhaps he does not err who says there are two uteruses, because there are two cavities like two hollow hands touching each other and covered by one panniculus terminated at one canal.

So that you may somewhat satisfy yourself about its form, place, and site, you may see the figures immediately following, to whose viewing let no one come who is not talented and expert in lines and shadow, as in a picture, which is of much assistance to physicians and many other artisans. The innate complexion of the uterus actuated by influence is warm and humid. Its services are to purge the body of its natural bloody superfluity but principally to conserve the species.

It can suffer all manner of ills. It often falls forward and can be entirely removed from the body, without injury to the health. I saw a diseased uterus extracted completely in the town of Carpi by my father. The woman to whom it belonged was cured and lived a long time.

I myself at Bologna extracted one entirely; it had cancer in it. The date was in May, 1507; the woman survived in good health.

In my presence my nephew by my brother Damian extracted another diseased uterus entire in a company of doctors and many students on October 5, 1520. This last was of a woman named Gentile, the wife of Christopher Brianti of Milan, dwelling in Bologna in the district (*contrada*) called "lo Inferno," who at this hour, on November 10, 1522 (June 10, 1523, is in good health and carries on her family duties, and during coitus with her husband she emits semen and has her menstruations at the proper times, a noteworthy fact), is in good health and carries on her family duties.

If you seek further details, see my *Commentary on the Anatomy of Mundinus,* and you will have a discussion of the pregnant uterus and of many other matters. Let this suffice concerning the anatomy of the lower body cavity.

II. CONCERNING THE ANATOMY
OF THE MIDDLE CAVITY

HAVING viewed the foregoing, cut the middle body cavity where are located the vital members with which, for the sake of a better order and before the uppermost body cavity is anatomized, you will also see some members of the anterior part of the neck and some intrinsic and extrinsic parts of the face.

The parts to be examined first are the members of the chest, which is called cassus, clibanus, and, by some, thorax. In it are parts which contain and are contained.

Of those which contain, just as in the lower body cavity, some are common, others proper, and others still more proper [that is, some parts are shared by two cavities, others are almost exclusively contained in one cavity, and others are still more strictly located in only one cavity].

The common parts are all those surrounding the hollow of the chest; some are in front, others at the sides, and others behind.

Neither in this body cavity of the vital members [see translator's note to p. 37] nor in the cavity of the natural members [the lowest cavity] are placed the superior parts nor the parts considered inferior to them, just as in the highest body cavity [of the animal members, the head], because the anterior, lateral, and posterior parts in the cavity of the natural members are united. These parts form the lower portion of the cavity of natural members [the lowest cavity] and likewise form the upper portion of the cavity of the vital members. For the cavity of the natural members terminates in its highest place, the cavity of vital members in its lowest place just as at a point, and by the aforesaid parts this body cavity is surrounded above and that body cavity is surrounded below. The transverse septum, or diaphragm, mediates between these cavities and forms the highest part of the lower cavity and the lower part of the upper cavity. Since the transverse septum is common to both cavities, it is not considered proper to or determined for any containing part of the aforesaid cavities, but authors place it among the parts contained. It is nevertheless a part which is contained and also contains. It is said to be contained insofar as it is within the hollow of the body and said to be containing because, above, it contains the natural members and, below, the vital members.

I say therefore that the common anterior and lateral part of the middle cavity is called the chest. The posterior part is called the highest portion of the back, and, placing the neck in the back, they call this middle part of the cavity the middle of the back.

Of the proper parts, some are in front, others at the sides, and others behind. Those in front are commonly regarded as three, that is, upper, lower, and middle.

The upper part is the place where immediately under the neck two bones are joined on both sides extending laterally toward the shoulders. These two bones are called the lateral forks [furculae], and this part is called the upper fork, receiving its name from the form and place, occupying a small space especially in the longitude of the chest. This place is called iugulum and clavis by some.[1]

Immediately under this is the middle part properly called chest [pectus], so called because the pexa is among the outstanding parts of the breasts. This part extends from the first aforementioned part below, up to a point near the transverse septum along its length. In its width it is as great as the width of the chest bones, with the exception of the ribs.

The lower part is the place where the aforesaid bones of the chest terminate near the region of the transverse septum. Because such bones extend laterally, they also make a fork. Thus this place is called the lower fork. In its middle there is a shield cartilage called pomegranate because it resembles part of the balaustium,[2] that is, the flower of the wild pomegranate.

The lateral parts are called ribbed and the sides and the region of the breasts.

Of the posterior parts, some are middle and some lateral. The middle parts are called interscapilium and metaphrenon and noton. The lateral parts are called scapulae, spatulae, and scapilium. Some, however, call the lateral with the middle parts metaphrenon and noton.

Of the more proper parts, some are anterior, others lateral, and others posterior.

Those in front are first the skin, the fat, some muscles, bones, cartilages, and the panniculus of the pleura.

The lateral parts are the skin, fat, substance of the breasts, many of the muscles, ribs, and also the panniculus of the pleura.

Last are the posterior parts, that is, skin, fat, muscular flesh and simple non-muscular flesh filling some hollows of the bones, twelve vertebrae of the ribs or chest, and the panniculus of the pleura.

The parts contained are the muscle of the diaphragm, called the transverse septum, which according to some is to be numbered among the contents of the chest insofar as its principal operation is to serve the heart by means of its motion, through which it moves the lung. Then there is the mediastinal panniculus, the capsule of the heart, the heart with its aorta artery, and the lung with its vessels, the chilis vein ascending, the nerves descending and ascending [called reversive], the gland called thymus and morus (mulberry), the gullet, that is, the path of the food from the mouth to the stomach, with the panniculi covering the aforesaid members.

The substance of this body cavity is made up of skin, fat, bones, cartilage, muscle, and panniculi.

Its bones are not united as in the head but are divided. So that the chest may be made obedient to the motion of the breath, therefore because of its motion, there are muscles in it. Galen said (*On the Usefulness of the Parts* vii [21]) that if the chest were made of muscles alone, these would fall on the heart and lung so that thus a certain space would be made within; but in order that the whole organ may be moved at once, the muscles are placed alternately with the bones.

This body cavity is called the chest. It is outstanding in size because it serves many large members. It has a larger hollow behind than in front. The beginning of the hollow is toward the rear, from the first vertebrae beneath the neck to the transverse septum as much as twelve ribs contain, but anteriorly it occupies only so much space as is contained inclusively between the upper and lower forks.

In man the chest is broad but not supplied with a shell as among the larger share of the brute beasts. Nevertheless, it is broader in man than in woman. For carrying the foetus the lower body cavity is larger in woman than in man, and because this is the region of the kidneys, os sacrum, and anchae, it is very wide in woman.

The form, number, and site of the chest are apparent, but its inner cavity is similar to the cavity of half an egg cut obliquely through its width. The part of this cavity toward the neck is sharper. It is also similar to the hoof of an ox, as is the form of the lung.

The chest is attached to the whole body. Its complexion is according to its parts; its innate complexion actuated by influence is warm. Its services are to guard the heart and lung principally. It suffers ills of all kinds.

CONCERNING THE BREASTS

In the anterior part of the chest toward the sides there are two round members. They are called breasts [mamillae], taking their name from their form, called rumae [figs] by the ancients. In the middle of each of them there is one little tubercle which is called the nipple [papilla], by which the infant sucks. Around the nipple there is a circle which is reddish or rosy and sometimes blackish. It is called phos in Greek. The substance of these breasts is made of veins, arteries, and nerves. Between them there is an empty space which is filled with white glandulous flesh that lacks sensation.

Because of its whiteness, sometimes the blood, having delayed in the breasts, is made white and and becomes milk. The breast changes the color of blood from red to white and makes milk just as the liver changes the color of the chyle to red and makes blood. For each one of these members changes the humidity [or liquid] contained in it to the nature and color of its own appearance. One part of this whitened blood nourishes the breasts; the other part is milk, a useful superfluity.

Their veins and arteries come to the breasts by descending from the region of the upper parts of the arm [*ascellae*] near the ribs.[3] Also from the region of the pubic bone through the abdomen come the veins which you saved previously. These veins and arteries appear best in an emaciated body, for they are hidden in a fat body. They are seen at their very best in a foetus of three or four months.

The number and size of the breasts are evident. They are, however, larger in woman than in man because milk must be generated. Their site is in the chest; it is broad and not equipped with a shell; in it they can comfortably be located, also because the superfluity of the upper members does not pass into hair, teeth, or horns as in brute animals. The breasts are attached to the brain by nerves, to the heart by arteries, to the liver and uterus by veins. From the uterus they receive the greater part of the blood from which milk is made. Therefore those women who are giving milk do not menstruate except rarely and little. In women who do not menstruate at the time when they should menstruate, the breasts swell. They swell and are also sore a little before the time of menstruation because the uterus and the veins attached to it are full.

Their services in the male are for decoration and for guarding the members of the chest. They send back heat to the heart. Sometimes milk is made in the male because of the abundance of nutriment, especially in a man who has large strong breasts. In women they perform the services just mentioned, but principally they are used for creating milk so that the newborn may be nourished with it until the child can swallow solid food. Milk is a nutriment adapted for the newborn because it is made from the blood by which the child was nourished before in the womb. The breasts suffer all kinds of ills.

CONCERNING THE MUSCLES OF THE CHEST

Having seen and noted the foregoing, you can remove the skin of the entire chest, leaving the muscles in their place, and cut through the breasts so that you may see their substance, especially the flesh in which there are veins and arteries scattered throughout. You will see that the nipples have many quite small foramina from which the milk comes forth. At these foramina,[4] according to some, terminate the extremities of the veins just mentioned through which the milk issues; according to others, the milk goes out from the sponginesses of the flesh of the breast that end at the foramina of the nipples and not immediately from the veins. Each view is possible.

Having inspected these, you will note in the chest many muscles which move the chest voluntarily,[5] although the chest is also moved involuntarily, that is, at the motion of the heart and the lung, as I have said in my *Commentary*. Some of these muscles are exterior, others between the ribs, and others inside the chest.

Of the exterior muscles, two are under the upper forks connected with the first rib; these stretch to the head of the scapula.[6] United with these there is another pair, of which each is unequal.[7] The first pair is double and makes itself into two parts. The upper part of this pair is connected with the neck and moves it.[8] The lower part moves the chest, and this pair is connected with a pair which is in turn connected with the fifth and sixth ribs.

Then there is another pair,[9] in the hollow of the scapula, connected with one pair that comes from the vertebrae of the scapula. In this all the muscles are as one pair connected with the posterior ribs.

Then there is another pair that arises from the sixth vertebra of the neck and from the first and second upper vertebrae of the chest connected with the same ribs.[10] All these muscles dilate the chest.

Then there is another pair extended under the roots of the upper ribs,[11] which in its descent is united with the extremities to one pair which is near the lower fork connected with the long muscles of the abdomen. Above this pair there are two pairs which cover the chest, and all these muscles contract the chest.

The muscles within the ribs dilate and contract,[12] differing among themselves in their work. The muscles between the ribs are four in number, between rib and rib, that is—two muscles toward the exterior and two toward the interior, which by gently separating you will recognize according to the nature of their villi. The first two above have transverse villi and dilate the chest. The second two below have broad villi and are the contracting muscles.

There is only one muscle within the chest, that is, the diaphragm, or transverse septum. When it is quiet, it contracts the chest by accident, however; when it is moved, it dilates the chest. The motion of the diaphragm is both voluntary and involuntary.

The number of all these muscles is one hundred and five, with the exception of the aforesaid muscles of the back and neck, that is, the two first muscles under the upper forks and two others connected with the fifth and sixth ribs, then two that come from the hollow of the scapula connected with the posterior ribs, then two from the sixth vertebra of the neck and from the first and second vertebrae of the chest connected with those same ribs. These muscles are eight in all, and all of them dilate or expand. There are the same number of muscles which contract, with the exception of the diaphragm, which also dilates.

Of the muscles which contract,[13] first there are two under the upper ribs and two around the lower fork. Above these muscles there are four others covering them. All these together with the diaphragm amount to seventeen. Then there are twenty-two spaces between the twenty-four ribs, and for each space there are four muscles. All of these eighty-eight are between the ribs, and together with the seventeen just mentioned they make the number of one hundred and five muscles.

But in order that all these may be well seen, the shoulder blades and back must also be skinned. First you will see the exterior muscles, next the muscles between the ribs. The diaphragm will be seen lower down in its place. These matters are more thoroughly discussed in my *Commentary on Mundinus*.

Note, reader, that the movements of the chest are four, that is, violent and non-violent exhalation and violent and non-violent inhalation, which the aforesaid muscles obey.

In the non-violent motion of inhalation the dilating muscles between the ribs perform their service; the movement of heart and lung also serves the same inhalation. When the diaphragm is moved, it draws the lung, which like an oven is filled with air, by the assistance of the dilating motion of the heart, and thus the chest dilates. The two first muscles which are near the upper forks also serve this motion. This motion, both voluntary and involuntary, is mixed with the involuntary, the dominant type of motion.

All the other muscles that dilate the chest come together with the afore-mentioned muscles and the diaphragm for violent inhalation. The motion of this inhalation is both voluntary and involuntary, with the voluntary uppermost while the heart is in good health.

For the non-violent motion of exhalation the inner muscles of the ribs and all the other contracting muscles come together, lightly however. This motion is principally involuntary because it is made by the heart and lung. The heart and lung assist the violent motion of exhalation, but principally all the contracting muscles and the muscles of the abdomen assist that motion.

From what has been said, the connection of the muscles of the chest is clear, as well as their form, site, size, and substance. Their number has been given. Their complexion is warm and humid. Their services have been described. They suffer all kinds of ills.

CONCERNING THE BONES OF THE CHEST

The bones of the chest do not form one continuous unit as in the head; there are many of them close to each other so that the chest can be expanded. Those in front and at the side are properly the bones of the chest, but those behind are more appropriate to the back. The lateral bones of the chest are called costae [ribs] by the Latins; in Greek they are called pleura, or pleuron, and chondron. There are twenty-four of them, twelve on each side. Of these the ten lower ribs, five on each side, are called rhoae in Greek. They are shorter than the others and (according to some) less bony than cartilaginous. The Latins call these the false and incomplete ribs. The higher ribs are complete and intact and are called the true ribs; there are seven of them on each side. To them is attached the aforementioned breastbone on either side because the bone in the middle is hard and, toward the ribs, cartilaginous, that is, because between breastbone and ribs there is cartilage.

This bone,[14] according to some, is made of seven bones to which on both sides are attached the seven true ribs. According to some others, it is formed of fifteen bones, that is, from seven on each side and one in the middle. According to still others, it is formed from twenty-one bones, that is, seven in the middle and on both sides from seven cartilages to which are attached the true ribs. (However, in the year 1523 in a public anatomy one true rib appeared double where it was joined to the bones of the chest.)

Their form is crescent-moon–shaped. Their substance, size, and site are clear. The ribs are attached to the twelve first vertebrae below the neck and to the aforesaid bones of the chest and to the panniculi covering them. Their complexion is cold and dry. Their services are evident. They suffer all kinds of ills.

Their anatomy you would best see if you could turn your attention to them alone in an individual, paying no attention to spiritual members.

CONCERNING THE PLEURA PANNICULUS

Among the members that contain is included the panniculus immediately adhering to the ribs and bones of the chest, which is called the pleura.[15] Its substance is sinewy, hard, and thin. From it arise the panniculi immediately covering the members in this body cavity. Its form is flat, extended throughout in the circumference of the chest; it also extends toward the upper part of the diaphragm and adheres continuously and very firmly to the diaphragm. Its size is evident from what has been said. It occupies the entire cavity of the chest with the exception of a certain part of the anterior which is occupied by the mediastinus.

Its number, site, connections, and complexion are evident. Its services are to clothe and guard the members of the chest, to bind its bones together, and to mediate between the bones and members contained in the chest lest what is soft be injured by what is very hard. It suffers all sorts of ills. You will not see this panniculus perfectly unless you cut the ribs and open the chest in the manner which will be described below.

CONCERNING THE TRANSVERSE SEPTUM, OR DIAPHRAGM

Having seen the parts which contain, we turn to those contained. First we must look at the pannicular muscle called the diaphragm, next the mediastinal panniculus, and third the panniculus called the capsule and receptacle of the heart.[16] After these members the heart will be examined and the rest of the contents of the chest.

I say that within the body between the lowest body cavity and the middle body cavity there is a certain pannicular and fleshy substance attached to the back near the twelfth vertebra which is attached to the back toward the front. It always terminates at the extremities of the false ribs and is attached to the end of the lower fork of the chest. Thus it divides the natural from the vital members.[17] This member is called the transverse septum, paries, phrenes, and diaphragm (Galen in his book *On the Voice and Breath* calls it percordium [1535]), because it is a muscle and not a panniculus. Nevertheless, it performs the function of a panniculus in guarding the heart and the higher members from the vapors of smells raised by the members of nutrition. Its fleshy part is at its extremity, and its tendons are in its center connected with the lung because it has to move the lung in such a location.

The pleura is connected to the diaphragm throughout toward the upper part, and in the same way in its lower part the siphac is connected with the diaphragm. The diaphragm is perforated toward the back by the ascending chilis vein, from which there remain in itself two veins that nourish the diaphragm, one on the right, the other on the left.[18] The descending aorta artery also perforates the diaphragm toward the back. The gullet, or meri, which is attached immediately to the stomach toward the lower body cavity, perforates the diaphragm.

Its form and size are evident. Its substance, connections, and site have been described. It is attached by small arteries to the heart, and to the brain by three pairs of nerves.[19] Of these, two come from the nape of the neck and one from the brain. These sometimes appear notable.

Its complexion is warm and humid. Its services have been told in part. Galen said that the origin of breathing and of all the forces of the body lay in the diaphragm. He was the first to discover these services. It assists also in expelling some of their contents from the stomach, the intestines, and the uterus. It provokes laughter, according to some, by moving the mind involuntarily in ticklings.

It suffers ill of all kinds; its rupture is fatal.

CONCERNING THE MEDIASTINUS

After the anatomy of the diaphragm there comes the mediastinal panniculus, so called because it divides the hollow of the chest along its longitude through the middle. (Galen calls it the descending coopertoria and Avicenna the middle panniculus.) It also has other names. This we must examine. First separate the bones of the chest from the ribs on right and left. Taking care not to damage the contents of the chest, separate also the diaphragm toward the front from the bones of the chest, and you will see that this panniculus divides the chest from bottom to top and from front to back. Its substance is pannicular. Its form and size are evident. Its site has been mentioned. The panniculi are two in number toward the anterior part, noticeably distant from each other with a notable hollow in themselves. Toward the back there appears one single panniculus connected to the pleura, from which according to some it arises. It is also connected to the diaphragm, back, and lung by means of a panniculus that originates from the pleura. It is also connected with the gullet, according to Avicenna, and to the bones of the chest. It is attached to the brain by nerves, to the heart by arteries, and to the liver by veins. Its complexion is frigid and dry. Its services are to divide the chest and lung through the middle so that if harm comes to one part it may not come to the other. It also guards the upper forks. A conservation of the heat of the heart is made by the mediastinus. It suffers all kinds of ills.

CONCERNING THE CAPSULE OF THE HEART

Having viewed the foregoing, you must lift up the anterior bones of the chest, separating them from the anterior part of the mediastinal panniculus. Place this in its position until you have seen the anatomy of the lung. Lift up also the highest parts of the ribs so that you may have ample space for viewing other items. In this section you will carefully look at the bones of the chest and the pleura. Leave the entire diaphragm in its place where you can, especially where it is connected to the back, so that the nerves which come to it from the upper parts may be seen and so that the connections of the gullet, or meri, with the diaphragm may be seen.

Having lifted these up, you will see the lung, in the middle of which there is one panniculus attached to the mediastinus; this is hard and thick so that it may better protect the heart from external harm. The form of this panniculus is like the inner member it contains, called the heart, which is concave and similar to a pouch. It is therefore called the capsule (and pericardia), in which is the heart itself and water in notable quantity bathing the heart and preventing it from drying out with strong heat. If the heart is dried out, cardiac illness will set in, by which the living creature is led into a decline as happened to Galen's ape. This capsule is very sensitive and strongly created for being filled up with the heart primarily. Its substance, site, form, services have been described. Its number is one, its size evident. It is attached to the pannicular roots of the heart, and to the pleura, mediastinus, and diaphragm by its skins; to the liver by veins, to the heart by arteries, to the brain by nerves. Its innate complexion is frigid and dry; its influence is warm because it is close to the heart. It suffers all kinds of ills.

Put back the capsule, mediastinus, and diaphragm into their place until you have seen the anatomy of the nerves that descend. These in their descent to the lower cavity send branches to the aforesaid members, as will be told below.

CONCERNING THE HEART

After the capsule comes the heart, whose anatomy as well as that of the lung and of some parts of the head and neck, because of their skilful composition and operation, I shall describe more at length.

For the dignity of the heart prevails over other parts since it is the chief of all the members and is called the sun of the microcosm because it illuminates the other members with its spirit. The heart has an especial heat. It certainly beats and has motion as if it were a living creature. Thus it is said to be formed first of all in the uterus for those who are to be born. Then are formed the brain and liver and very late the eyes, as some think, but these are the first to die. The heart dies last. This member alone is not weakened by ills, though it does not escape the punishments of life; but when it is perceptibly injured, it brings death at once. When the other parts are corrupted, its vitality endures, and because of this that living creature does not survive in whose heart some injury is found, as it may survive injuries in other parts of the body.

Living creatures whose hearts are small are bold. Timid, however, are those whose hearts are very large in proportion to their bodily size, as mice, the rabbit, the donkey and the deer. For all timid creatures or those made vicious through fear nevertheless have a large heart strong with much spirit, which makes them occasionally bolder than other creatures.

Some men are said to be born with a shaggy heart; they are bolder and stronger than other men, as, for example, Aristomenes the Messenian, who killed three hundred Spartans and when wounded and captured finally escaped by fleeing into the hiding place of foxes. Captured once more, he boldly fled again. Captured a third time by the use of traps, the Spartans cut open his chest to find the cause of his virility and discovered that his heart was bristly with hair (according to Pliny). There is a heart likewise in all creatures which have a transverse septum and blood, according to Aristotle, *History of Animals* ii. 15. In some, however, it cannot be seen because of its small size.

The site of the heart is in the middle of the chest within the lung. In man it declines only with its lowest part to the left nipple so that it may not touch the bones of the chest, which are not covered with shell as in brute creatures but are compressed through the breadth of the chest.

It has the form of a pyramid, humped however, not principally because it is hot, following the form of fire, but because it is mixed, perfect, and animate and so possesses a form suitable for its operation.

Its highest part is broad where it seeks the upper regions and is attached to the back.[20] This part is the nobler of the parts of the heart because by means of the two orifices of the arteries of the left side,[21] coming from this part, the life of the living creature is preserved. In the lowest part it collects itself into a sharp point and becomes almost like a sword; its anterior part is prominent.

Its humped part also faces toward the upper region of the chest and takes such a form so that its upper and lower structure may be good and so that a superfluity may not exist in it apt to impede its continuous motion and so that in its cuspid [pointed end] it may be gathered up at one movement in order that the area which is injured by the touch of the bones may be the the least part of the heart, to receive a lesser injury.

Its substance is of simple flesh solid everywhere. It has the left part of itself and of its sharp point of thicker flesh to preserve the spirit located there and so that its weight may balance the weight of blood contained in the right ventricle, whose walls are lighter than those of the left ventricle.

In its hollows are many white ligaments with many little pieces of flesh existing therein.[22] The ligaments are attached to the chilis vein,[23] as well as to the arterious vein, with little skins,[24] or ostiola.

The heart is inclosed by a thin, strong membrane with some fat, both of which conserve and strengthen its substance and heat and prevent it from drying out.

At the top where it adheres to the back are two little skins, wrinkled and concave, called auricles, which are united to its domiciles[25] [atria], or ventricles, on right and left. These like a good housekeeper receive and preserve its spirit and superfluous blood and afterward give it back when necessary. (In the right auricle blood is kept, but in the left auricle spirit and air are kept.)

Nature ordered these auricles so that they might receive the blood (and air coming from outside) and (vital) spirit occasionally overflowing in the heart, supplying the changes of the magnitude of the heart, by which it might have occupied the places of the other members near to itself.

Because of its magnitude it might have been heavy and unfit for motion; and frequently also, if it were very large, it would be empty for lack of spirit and blood and consequently weak as it is in timid animals that have a large heart, that is, one empty in proportion to blood and spirit.

Its roots are attached to the highest part of itself. These are solid and hard, as if cartilaginous, so that above these its continuous agile motion may take place.

In the heart there are multiformed fibers [inuli] located in diverse manner so that it may sustain continuous, strong motions which are involuntary and not voluntary, and therefore there is not any muscle [lacertus] in it.

In the highest part of the heart on its outside is a vein which originates from the chilis vein and which changes into very small branches obliquely toward the point of the heart on each side. This vein nourishes the heart.[26]

In the same place also there are two pulsating veins running on the outside that originate from the aorta.[27] One is in the same location where is found the non-pulsating vein mentioned above; this vein keeps the heart alive. Another vein is spread out in the right sinus and brings the vital force to it. It also prepares and vivifies the blood that continuously enters the sinus. By means of this vein through the mediation of the chyle the liver in its hump [gibbus] is rid of secretions and conserves its own vitality.

The heart possesses a triple sinus,[28] or hollow or domicile [atrium] or ventricle. The right one is larger than the left. The left sinus reaches to the extremity of the point [cuspis] of the heart. The right sinus terminates a little under that place.

Between these sinuses is a dense, thick wall called diaphragm by Galen.[29] In this wall there are many little foramina stretching from the right sinus to the left sinus.[30] They are broader at the right sinus than at the left sinus. These foramina are dilated when the heart is shortened and opens; they are contracted when the heart is elongated and closes. Hence the blood, made thin and prepared, passes from the right to the left, where it is completely changed into vital spirit.

These orifices are considered by physicians as the middle sinus. This sinus, according to Avicenna, Galen calls the pit [fovea] and meatus and not ventricle, so that it may be the receptacle of nourishment by which the heart is fed. This nourishment is very thick, similar to the substance of the heart. It is a mine of the spirit generated in the heart by the thin blood and it prevails [suddit] because the more temperate [more thin] blood is in the middle ventricle.[31]

The right sinus has at its highest part two veins.[32] The tunic of one of these is simple. It is larger than the other veins, coming from the liver, and it is called chilis, concave, and boldly ascending [audax ascendens]. This vein is very large because it brings the blood to all the other veins within the heart and outside it.[33] It receives nothing from them, and therefore it carries more blood into the heart than it may carry back. This vein is also very large so that it may contain the blood which flows back and forth many times in large quantity and so that the vein may bring it to the heart in a brief space and so that by the heart the blood may be more properly prepared.

This blood so prepared is divided into three parts. One part, of thin bilious blood, is smaller than the others and goes to nourish the lung.

Another part, larger than the one just mentioned, and thinner, goes through the foramina of the diaphragm to the left sinus,[34] where it is turned into spirit.

The third part is not so thin, and because it is far greater in quantity than the other two parts of the blood, it passes often in and out of the right sinus so that it may be completely prepared and take up vitality;[35] through the chyle itself it passes to all parts of the living creature and nourishes them.

Avicenna, however, places a fourth part of the blood which he says is temperate in the middle ventricle; yet this is unknown to my eyes, perhaps because in the middle wall of the heart there penetrates the blood that nourishes it, but the blood passes (in a brief space) into the substance of that which is nourished, since in that place there is no blood outside the veins, according to my judgment, except in the right and left ventricles.[36]

The highest (a certain) orifice of this vein terminates at the heart. While the heart is dilated and draws the blood, this orifice is opened, and while the heart is contracted (expelling it), it is closed with the expulsion, but not completely since it remains partly open. Thus always in this orifice like a treasure house and mine of heat nature retains some portion of the hot blood. This portion changes the blood that comes to it afresh into its own nature by uniting that blood with itself.

This orifice is opened and closed by three sinewy or ligamentous little skins whose color is white; these skins are attached with their upper extremities to the walls of the aforesaid sinus by white solid ligaments.

These skins are called ostiola. They are opened completely to the inner part of the sinus, yielding to the entering blood, and are closed on the outside but not completely. These skins are solid and hard; so are the skins of the arterious vein in order that in the great and continuous movements of the heart disruption may not come to them because the skins are attached to its highest part by ligaments continually extending them.

The skins of the aorta artery and of the arterial vein are less hard than these because they are not extended by any ligaments; therefore they lack the fear of disruption.

Another vein goes to the lung.[37] The name of this vein is non-pulsating, or quiet. It is also called the arterial vein, and it is called a vein because it carries the blood to the lung to nourish the latter. It is called arterial because it possesses two tunics. It is made strong and compact because the thin, bilious blood passes through it and so that it may not burst because of its continuous motion. In its orifice there are three skins,[38] or ostiola, that close themselves completely within the sinus; outside, by opening themselves they yield to the blood that goes forth. In the dilation of the heart they are completely closed so that the blood may not regurgitate to the lung. In the heart's contraction, however, they are opened and adhere to the walls of the vein. Nor are they anywhere united by ligaments as the first skins are.

The substance of these skins is pannicular. Their form is similar to the vacuity which exists within the letter C. Therefore they are called C-shaped ostiola. They also have that circular form which the human fingernail has. These skins are attached to the body of the vein with their circular part.

The left sinus is nobler than the others because to it minister first the right and middle sinus, and also because of the spirit it contains it prevails over the others. It has two veins in its highest part[39]—the large one not much smaller than the chilis vein mentioned before, which is like a branch distributed to the whole body. This vein is pulsating and has two tunics. Their thickness, according to Herophilus, is six times that of the vein. This is called the aorta artery, and it is larger. Its inner tunic is harder than the outer tunic so that it may withstand the percussion and the substance of the spirit for whose custody it is intended.[40]

This artery leads the vital spirit to the entire body of the living creature and maintains it during life.[41]

Through this artery, said Galen, all the members except the lung breathe in and out lest their vitality be suffocated. The veins are, as it were, the repositories of the food, requiring neither diastole nor systole, and therefore their body is thin, porous, and smooth. The lung, however, breathes in and out because of the motion of the heart and chest.

This artery or its branches are rarely without the chilis vein as a companion. The aorta ascending is divided in two a little above the heart. One part twists in an oblique direction to the lower region and descends. This part in the chest and lowest body cavity sends many fibers from itself down to the feet and keeps alive their members. Under this branch slanted off below they ascend by the left nerves of the voice which are called reversive,[42] and this place is called flexor and girgilus, concerning which we shall speak elsewhere.

Another part ascends near part of the lung, the thymus gland, the highest region of the chest, the arms, neck, and head and fills their parts with vitality and spirit.

Always those arteries which are attached to the veins by many pores or little fibers unite with each other or come together by coastomosis [placing their mouths together]. The vein drinks in the artery,[43] and, contrariwise, the artery drinks in the vein, and the blood passes from the vein into the artery. Within the latter the blood is made spiritual in necessity, and from the artery into the vein passes the vital spirit **preparing** its blood and preserving the blood in its virtue. Their tunics also are nourished and vivified by their contents. This artery above the heart is smaller than below, according to Galen, *On the Usefulness of the Parts* xvi. 11, and is made such because from the heart below there are more animal parts than there are above the heart. So much larger is the descending artery than the artery ascending through the back as the multitude of lower parts exceeds the number of higher parts. Herein is recognized the no small justice of nature. The descending chilis vein must also be larger than the ascending vein for the same reason.

In the orifice of this pulsating vein, which is called auritium, there are three **C**-shaped ostiola which open and close at the same time and in the same manner as the arterial vein opens and closes.[44]

There is another non-pulsating vein in this ventricle.[45] It is quiet and called the venal artery; it is called artery because it carries the spirit or air back and forth to the heart and from the heart to the lung, from which the air is sent outside the chest. It is called a vein because it has a simple tunic. In the orifice of this vein are only two little skins or ostiola attached in the same fashion and incompletely,[46] opening and closing with the dilation and contraction of the heart by which they make the ostiola in the orifice of the chilis vein. This arterial vein brings more air to the heart than it carries outside because from the blood and air introduced by this vein the vital spirit is generated, which passes through the aorta to all the parts of the living creature.[47]

From what has been said the connections, complexion, and services of the heart are evident. Its size is conspicuous. Its number is one, although the heart of an ape has been found to have two heads in an unnatural fashion. It is also said that in Paphlagonia the partridges have two hearts. All kinds of diseases can occur to the heart; nevertheless, it does not withstand them if they last long.

CONCERNING THE LUNG

The heart being examined, next comes the lung. It is called a fan [flabellum] and a flail [ventilabrum] in Latin and pneumon in Greek. It is the originator of breathing and the workshop of the air, whence the soul is nourished as the body is with food. The lung is near the heart. It fills the hollow of the chest with its five envelopes, or lobes.[48] Two of these are on the left, three rather more on the right. Of these three lobes one is smaller than the others. It adheres to the back just about in the middle; it has little pipes [fistulae] but almost no motion.[49] This lobe is a cushion for the ascending chilis vein. Near that envelope toward the upper part there is a certain adenous flesh which is, together with the lobe just mentioned, a cushion or mattress for the aforesaid vein. This flesh is of notable size, and by authors it is called morus and thymus and by laymen it is named "little soul" [animella] and laticinium; it is found in ordinary foods of a savory taste, especially the food found in calves and milk kids.

The substance of the lung is mixed and of rare, light, smooth flesh; it is reddish in color, shading off to white similar to the foam of coagulated blood. The substance is also made up of three vessels,[50] or pipes, spread out like a net through all parts of the lung in the same manner as the branches of the chilis vein (and portal vein) are spread out in the liver. This composition is perhaps similar to that of a honeycomb and also a sponge. Therefore it is capable of holding blood and air. For the lung is, as it were, a sort of storehouse of air for the heart, fitted to serve both motions, dilation and contraction.

Its flesh is rare so that continuously there may be in it much blood and air. Two vessels in the lung which contain blood indicate the lung's size;[51] these vessels are larger than vessels in any other member of equal size, the heart and liver excepted. In the latter two members the vessels containing blood are larger not for their own sake indeed but because they bring spirit and blood to all the members.

Blood is in the lung in large amount because its bounteous supply is reduced through the lung's continual motion, which a great quantity continually resists. The blood is thin so that it may quickly penetrate to all parts of the lung to nourish it. It is also thin so that it may be light lest by its weight it should impede the motion of the lung. The long submersion of a living creature without suffocation indicates that there is a large amount of air also in the lung; and the long continuous emission of voice and breath, hindering the reception of new air; or when anyone shrinks back from drawing in air because of a stink or other causes. This air in submersions and in stinks is held in the mouth and jaws, the tonsils assisting with their little skins.

The service of this continually drawn air is that by means of it when previously altered the heart is cooled and made of moderate temperature in necessity; also that the heart may be relieved in order that it may not be suffocated. Its usefulness is also that from it in no small part may be generated the spirits necessary for existence and well-being. It is also of service in the expulsion of the superfluous, hot, and smoky air that is attracted, to allow the entrance of less warm air that has been altered previously in the lung and in the members through which it passes.

This smoky air like a burned excess of spirit is driven through the pulsing vein into the branches of the trachea by the heart's contraction and hence later with the help of the systolic motion of the lung through the trachea and through the nostrils and mouth it passes forth from the living creature.[52]

The air entering the heart has the beginning of its alteration in the nostrils, mouth, jaws, trachea, and the branches of the trachea dispersed in the lung in the same manner in which nourishment by food and drink has its alteration in the mouth, gullet, stomach, and liver.[53]

For the alteration in the air of the lung is comparable to the alteration in the chyle of the liver. Blood is made from chyle by the liver and receives its complete preparation in the heart. Spirit is prepared from air by the lung and is made truly vital in the heart. This air seeks the upper regions in the marvelous net [rete mirabile] or in the tiniest branchlets of the arteries near the brain and is once more altered.[54] Then, entering the ventricles of the brain, it is made completely into "animal" spirit, which is lucid, light, and pure.

The flesh of the lung is also light so that it may not impede the lung's motion. It is smooth so that it may guard the lung's vessels from rupture. It is ruddy, clear, shading off to white on account of the dominion of the air by which it is nourished and also because of its own frigidity.

A thin panniculus covers this substance of the lung,[55] made of many membranes arising (from its fistulae and) from the panniculus of the chest; by means of this panniculus the lung has sensation.

There are three fistulae of the lung,[56] one of which like the others, always diminishing, descends to all its parts, even to the panniculus inclusively enveloping the lung united to the gullet by the pharynx or epiglottis through the anterior part of the neck. This pipe is hard, always open, larger than the others, and composed of many cartilages each united near one another by pannicular ligaments. This pipe is called the trachea, rough artery, larynx, and bronchium. Its cartilages are complete in the lung and annular [ring-shaped]. They are incomplete in the neck and C-shaped. From their size and shape it is judged in their hawking or hemming whether there are ulcers in the extreme parts of the lung, in the middle parts, or in the neck.

Between these cartilages and in the entire trachea within and without there is a panniculus of medium substance, perfectly circular, attached to the jaws and mouth, in which there are villi which lengthen and shorten the trachea in the motions of the lung (and of the trachea itself).

The services of this panniculus are to preserve these cartilages from the entrance and exit of extraneous objects; it is also a lenitive of the voice.

This pipe carries no blood as the others do but air only. By this pipe alone extraneous objects contained in the chest are expelled which have entered it at the time of the lung's dilation by the thin panniculus that envelopes the lung. Thus expulsion of corrupt blood [sanies] and of other extraneous matter to the mouth and outside is effected without the heart being troubled.

This pipe also has the middle position among the others. On its right is a quiet vein,[57] on its left a pulsating vein.[58] The pulsating vein in the anterior part immediately outside the heart passes into the substance of the lung lest because of its motion and thinness it should be broken.[59] The non-pulsating vein,[60] since it has two tunics and is strong, does not immediately enter the lung, but, first surrounding the trachea tending toward the posterior region, it also enters the lung.

In this single internal organ not without cause the pulsating vein has changed substance (and content) with the non-pulsating vein.[61] For the non-pulsating is called the arterial vein. In the other members it is simple; in the lung it has two tunics, first, so that it may not be ruptured because of its continual motion and, second, so that it may also contain the thin blood which nourishes the flesh of the lung and also the trachea.

The pulsating vein called the arterial vein (venal artery) has a single tunic. It is agile in motion so that in brief space of time it may serve dilation and contraction. This vein leads the air to the heart and leads it out. In this vein also is spiritual blood, as some believe, which nourishes the lung; it rather gives the lung vitality. Its branches unite or come together in anastomosis with the branches of the trachea through which the lung gives air to the heart,[62] and the heart, not ungrateful, gives life and nutrition to the lung.

The branches of this vein are so narrow that the blood does not penetrate through them to the trachea. Thus they are passable for air and impassable for blood, since, if they are noticeably open, the blood flows from them to the trachea. Possibly, as some think, the blood also flows from the branches of the non-pulsating vein into the trachea where blood becomes spittle without the rupture of the veins of the chest. The pulsating vein is, however, more apt to suffer this [flow of blood into the trachea].

Each of the aforementioned five vessels at their first entrance into the lung divides into five branches, ever diminishing through all parts of the lung and multiplying branches. Two are on the left and three on the right; one of these, smaller than the others, goes to the small lobe on the right adhering more to the back: this vessel, as we said above, is a coverlet for the ascending chilis vein.

The form of the lung is like an ox's hoof. As to number, some think it has two members united into one, for this is the appearance of one lung with five lobes divided into two similar parts so that when one is injured the other may remain firm. In the posterior region it is longer than in front, following the location of the transverse septum. In number it is one. Its size, site, and connections are evident. Its complexion is warm on account of its contents and place. By accident, however, because of the phlegm which exists in it, the lung is considered cold. Its services are to assist preparation and carrying to the heart, and to serve the breathing, voice, and speech. Its little lobe serves the ascending chilis vein. It suffers ills of all kinds.

CONCERNING THE ANATOMY OF SOME PARTS OF THE
NECK AND OF THE PULSATING AND QUIET
VEINS ASCENDING FROM THE LIVER AND HEART
TO THE HEAD AND HANDS INCLUSIVELY

Having viewed the preceding in partial section, next would come the trachea, epiglottis, and gullet. These, however, cannot be well seen at the present unless the anatomy of some parts of the neck and of the face are examined first. When we have seen these latter parts, we shall discuss the former. The lung therefore having been disposed of, keep some of its upper fleshy part in order to examine the trunk of the trachea artery, laying the rest aside with the exception of the fifth lobe which adheres to the back. Save also a certain gland nearby, called the morus and thymus, so that above these may be seen the site of the chilis vein and the ascending artery for which these two members are a coverlet. You will also keep the heart, its capsule, the mediastinal panniculus, the stomach, and the transverse septum in their places in order to investigate other matters concerning them.

These parts being saved, for the sake of a better order I shall first begin discussing the anatomy of the neck. I say the neck is a noble organic member and very necessary to man because of the members contained in it. According to Aristotle, *On the Parts of Animals* iii. 3, the neck is made for preserving the trachea which assists the lung and for the gullet.

But Galen, *On the Usefulness of the Parts* viii (ix). 1, says the neck exists primarily for the lung, since creatures lacking a neck lack a lung, as fish do. He adds, however, that the neck is the path of those members which descend from the upper region to the lower and of those members which ascend from the lower to the upper region. Those which descend are nerves, the gullet, some muscles, and the nape of the neck. Those members which ascend are the pulsating and quiet veins. The nape of the neck is contained by vertebrae so that it may be safe from external injuries.[63] That vacancy between parts of the veins and arteries is filled by glands. All these are guarded by coverings and ligaments. Then everything is covered by skin. That which is composed of all these items is the neck, which is placed where it is on account of the reed [canna, windpipe] of the lung through which the voice and breathing are made. The neck also in some animals takes the place of a hand because they take their food from the earth with the help of their neck on account of the length of their feet. The neck is of this sort because it serves as the reed of the lung, and by its mediation the nerves pass to the arms, palms, diaphragm, and to the other members, under the leadership of the nape. Therefore because of the origin of the nerves the vertebrae of which the neck is composed have been placed between chest and head. This is what Galen says, but he does not say whether the trachea ascends or descends; and although he says the gullet descends, perhaps it also ascends: he cannot prove its descent any more than he can prove its ascent, nor likewise of the trachea since it has no manifest origin as the veins, arteries, and nerves have.

Let us say then for the present that the neck is considered that part upon which the head is sustained and turned; which serves the upper, the middle, and the lower body cavities by means of nerves descending from the brain and the nape; whose site is in front of the upper forks of the chest and behind the highest vertebra of the ribs, and on the sides from above the shoulders up to the bone of the head called basilar. The posterior part of the neck is also called cervix; we shall speak of this elsewhere. The anterior part is called the neck (and by some guttur, throat), and because this member exists chiefly for the sake of the trachea, it will be the nobler of these parts. The anatomy of the neck is to be placed with that of the trachea, because of this nobility and because the trachea is part of the lung, which is one of the more important parts of the middle body cavity mentioned before. Thus the anatomy of the neck for the present is to be taken with the anatomy of the middle body cavity.

This part named the trachea is called guttur and pharynx by many, although the pharynx according to some is made up of veins which swell in loud voices. These veins are called granges and fragitides [sphagitides] by Celsus, and by some sfragitides. These veins are called guidez by the Arabs, and apoplectic and veins of sleep, and by some pensiles, spermatic, juveniles, iugulares, and organic. By Galen in his book *On the Usefulness of the Parts* they are called fagotides because they are near the pathway of the food, and by some they are called carotides or veins of sleep. Celsus calls only the arteries in that place by the name carotides, from *caros,* which is sleep, because according to some for the most part a stoppage is made in the branches of these arteries which causes sleep and also apoplexy.

Of the veins on both sides there is one immediately below the skin which is commonly called guidez manifesta. On both sides also below some notable muscles of the neck there is one vein called guidez occulta and profunda [hidden and deep] which is a companion to the carotid artery.[64]

With these deep veins and arteries on both sides is associated a nerve of notable size which is called descending.[65] From these nerves on both sides there arise the reversive nerves;[66] concerning all of these I shall speak a little later.

The anterior part of the neck is called iugulum by some and by others gullet, although this is bad usage because the gullet is the pathway of food and drink and the iugulum is that part which is immediately above the upper forks of the chest. Some, however, call these forks the iugulum and clavis and clidas and clidia. The extremity of these forks toward the scapulae is called epomis; the other part toward the middle of the chest is called parasfagis [parasphagis].

Having noted the foregoing, next after the skin would come the anatomy of the muscles which move the neck and head; but we cannot hold a complete investigation of these unless the anatomy of their nerves, veins, and aforesaid arteries is disposed of. Therefore let us be silent about them, sending our readers to Galen, Avicenna, and to other authors. These muscles are numerous and located in different places; thus they should be examined with care. You should turn your attention to them alone, because they are difficult to anatomize. Because of this fact Galen, *On the Usefulness of the Parts* xii. 8, where he speaks of these muscles, says, "It is fitting for one to be trained carefully beforehand if he wishes to follow with certainty the things which are said here." In the same passage he also declares that speech alone is not sufficient in anatomy, but touch and sight are needed. Therefore let these authors be studied, because we must pay attention only to the neck and head, in which there are many muscles as near to the vertebrae as to any other place; these cannot be seen in ordinary anatomical investigation.

For the head has many movements made by means of the neck with its bones and muscles. Some of these movements, according to Avicenna, in the first part of Book I [of the *Canon*], are proper to the head and some common to it and to the five vertebrae of the neck by which the movement composed of the simultaneous declination of head and neck is made. These movements either curve forward or backward or to right or left, and among them is the motion of conversion or turning around. These muscles are many and large since their position is multiform and also because they have large and almost continuous movements. Therefore Galen said [*loc. cit.*] that they surround the head on all sides because they move it in any direction in which you wish to bend it. As to their number there is no agreement between Avicenna and some of his disputing colleagues.

Leaving their investigation in a partial state, cut the skin on the sides of the neck, laying bare the lateral and anterior muscles. Above these immediately under the skin you will note the vein guidez manifesta, which you saved unharmed. Then cut those large muscles descending obliquely from the ears to the upper forks toward the middle of the chest.[67] Under these on both sides is a gland (sometimes larger in one person than in another) shaped almost like an almond. This fills the vacant space existing therein between the veins and arteries near the lower part of the epiglottis. Therefore it is called the equalizer of the parts of the neck [*aequatrix partium colli*]; it moistens them when necessary. You will note, under these glands on both sides,[68] a notable guidez vein and likewise a companion artery to it,[69] which are called hidden and apoplectic; many names of these have been mentioned above.

Near the aforesaid arteries and veins you will also note on both sides one nerve composed of many villi or fibers. These nerves are called descending,[70] and from them arise the reversive nerves,[71] of which a fine investigation will later be made.

Save these nerves and the branches of the aforesaid artery and each vein, hidden and manifest, until you have seen the veins and arteries ascending from the heart and from the liver to this place. To examine these let the operator return to the region of the hump of the liver once more, and there he will note the large trunk of the ascending chilis vein,[72] which in its ascent perforates the transverse septum and there on both sides sends out many veinlets. Two of these feed the transverse septum; the others nourish the lower ribs and the members near these.

A very large branch of this trunk of the chilis vein ascends up to the heart, loose all the way, without an artery to accompany it. Through this branch the hump of the liver relieves itself of secretions and is perhaps vivified.

This branch is divided into three parts. One of these,[73] much smaller than the others, enters the roots of the heart, is disseminated through the heart's substance, and nourishes it.

Another part is larger than the others; it is united with the right atrium of the heart and brings a very copious supply of blood to it.

According to some, that vein called arterial which nourishes the lung draws its origin from this branch. Of these veins, however, I have spoken somewhat in the dissection of the heart.

The third branch of those just mentioned, which is also outstanding,[74] ascends from the region of the heart and above it. Under this there is a certain glandulous flesh called morus and thymus, and this together with the fifth lobe of the lung which adheres to the back, as I have said above, is the cushion for the aforesaid ascending branch up to the highest fork of the chest, where this vein is divided into two branches passing on the right and on the left transversely toward the shoulder blades.[75] In this fashion also the great artery called aorta ascending passes transversely toward the shoulder blades, and, so that you may better see these veins and arteries, lay aside the upper forks. Do so carefully, however, so that you do not loosen the members near to them.

Having disposed of these, you must see the aforesaid veins and arteries,[76] first noting that each of these is divided into two branches. One of these branches, both of the vein and of the artery, on both sides ascends to the head by way of the neck. From these branches arise all the veins of the neck called guidez;[77] these you will keep to examine more closely later on.

The other branch also on both sides is divided into five parts. One of them nourishes the higher ribs,[78] one nourishes the place of the shoulder blades,[79] one nourishes the submerged muscles of the neck,[80] and one penetrates into the upper vertebrae of the neck and from there passes to the head.[81] Branches of the pulsating vein accompany these parts.

Another branch, larger than all those mentioned, passes to the axilla, or armpit,[82] and here it is divided into four branches. One of these is spread out in the muscles located above the chest which move the shoulder blades.[83] One passes into the loose flesh and into certain panniculi of the armpits.[84] One passes from the highest part of the chest around the breasts,[85] descending toward the abdomen, and here, according to some, it nourishes the breasts. In part it carries the material of the milk to them; it is coupled in the abdomen, as I have said elsewhere, with a vein ascending from the groin and from the uterus to the breasts. It is of this branch that Galen, *On the Usefulness of the Parts* xiv. 8, speaks when he says that the veins pass from the thorax to the hypochondria and to the entire epigastrium and are coupled with veins which are carried from the lower region to the uterus. These veins have connections so that when the living creature grows in uteruses the veins bring nourishment to it. When the infant is born, the veins swell out the breasts again; therefore it does not happen that menstruation and lactation can be well carried on together.

Another branch larger than the aforementioned branches is on both sides divided into three branches. One passes to the muscles which are in the shoulder blades,[86] one to the muscles of the armpits,[87] another, larger than the foregoing, passes through an inner path toward the adiutorium,[88] and here it goes to the little hand. This branch is called axillary and basilica; when it is phlebotomized, it is of comfort in ailments of the chest because of its connections near to the true ribs and to the entire chest. This vein is vulgarly called the vein of the liver because it is nearer to the liver than is the cephalic vein.

From the first veins I asked you to save from which the guidez veins are made, one ascends on both sides. Before they ascend far, they are divided into two parts. One of them is called guidez manifesta because it is near the skin. It is likely to be easily seen, because in the living body it swells with a loud voice. The other part because it is below some muscles is called guidez profunda et submersa.

The guidez manifesta as soon as it ascends above the fork is divided on both sides into two parts, one of which ascends; the other, however, is wound around near the fork. From this part arise many branches that nourish the parts near themselves, and some of these branches ascend again and are once more united with the previously mentioned first branch of the guidez manifesta. But before they are united, one notable branch passes to the shoulder blade and through the exterior part under the skin of the adiutorium and terminates at the little hand.[89] This branch is called the scapular, humeral,

and cephalic, because it leads from the head on account of the very close connection which this branch has with its guidez which nourishes the head. But
of this cephalic vein and also of the basilica and of the artery which accompanies the latter we shall speak at greater length in the special anatomy of
the large and small hand.

The aforesaid guidez manifesta is notable on both sides. It is immediately
under the skin above the muscles of the neck. With its branches it nourishes
the upper and lower jaws,[90] the tongue,[91] and head,[92] ascending through the
exterior part around the ears.

Some wish to call these branches of guidez manifesta which are around
the ears spermatic veins,[93] because, they say, the sperm comes by way of them
from the brain. These men say this because of the words of Hippocrates in
his work *On Air and Water,* where he said that whoever had the veins behind his ears cut was completely deprived of all ability to generate offspring.
There are some, however, who think such veins are from the branches of
guidez profunda which nourish the muscles that exist between the first and
second vertebrae of the neck, and some say Hippocrates understood by veins
the arteries themselves, since they are more fitted for good sperm than the
veins. In the same passage Hippocrates says the sperm comes from the entire
body, and Avicenna [*Canon*], Fen XX. iii. 3, says Galen did not know
whether an incision of these veins would cause sterility or not but nevethe-
less said that sterility would occur through incision of these veins. But it
seems to me that it is not necessary for sperm to come from the brain alone,
although it is fomented in the brain. By a good anatomy of the spermatic
vessels the knowledge is brought forth that the incision of these veins behind
the ears does not make one sterile on account of the sperm that descends
through the veins. The incision of these veins can, however, weaken the
brain to such an extent that it does not transmit as it should the animal spirit
for conception. This the guidez profunda can do better than the guidez manifesta, and the arteries can do better than the veins because they are carriers of
spirit. Each view, nevertheless, is possible.

The guidez profunda on both sides near the meri, or gullet, ascends below
the aforesaid muscles which you have cut, and in its ascent it sends out
branches which nourish the gullet and the muscles of the pharynx. They also
nourish the muscles that exist between the first and second vertebrae of the
neck. From these arise, according to some, the spermatic veins mentioned by
Hippocrates which are behind the ears, concerning which the final verdict
has not yet been handed down. They also nourish the pericranium, ascending
through it from the bottom to the very top of the head; there, perforating the
cranium, they descend into the dura and pia mater, bringing (some) nourishment to them.

From the aforesaid deep vein arises one branch on both sides,[94] perforating the basilar bone in the direction of the lambdoid suture [commissura]. Sustained by the dura mater, it ascends up to the top of the head.[95] From this vein in that place many branches go out through the pores of the cranium which also nourish the pericranium. The greater part of the aforesaid branches ascending within the skull with the dura mater pass into the pia mater. With these there also pass some branches of the aforesaid guidez manifesta,[96] penetrating the skull at its top from the outside to the inside part, and from here they pass into the substance of the brain and nourish it.

Of the aforesaid branches some in the direction of the sagittal and lambdoid sutures enter the dura mater, which is doubled in that place. This place is like a press [torcular] by which the blood is pressed out from the aforesaid veins into a certain ample location existing there near the exterior.[97] This is called the broad way (platea), pit (fovea), palmentum [palm grove?], and pool [lacuna]. Near this platea are certain veins which suck the pressed-out blood into it; these nourish the center of the brain with this same blood. All these veins within the cranium together with the arteries are those from which is formed (the net called secundinum) what is rightly called secundinum or otherwise the pia mater.

The aforesaid arteries called carotids, which exist in the neck near the guidez (profunda) veins and the descending nerves, ascending on both sides of the neck with some branches scattered in front and behind pass to the tongue,[98] the upper and lower jaws,[99] and to the entire face,[100] and into the back part of the head [occipitium, occiput].[101] Some notable arteries pass near the ears in the temples. With their branches they stretch to the top of the head, and some also stretching to the muscles near a common juncture are spread out in the neck and head where there is a large foramen from which the spinal medulla comes forth. It was by these branches perhaps that Hippocrates said the sperm descended from the brain, because the ancients called arteries also veins; and that is why he said this. Avicenna [*Canon*], Fen XX. iii, said these veins were continued to the nape of the neck so that they might not be far away from the brain.[102] In these veins there is a light milky blood which goes first to the kidneys, then after them to the veins which pass to the testicles.[103] One notable branch of these arteries on both sides perforates the basilar bone toward the front and is united with the pia mater, vitalizing the brain and carrying spirits to the brain's ventricles.[104]

From this branch ascended on both sides immediately above this basilar bone, according to the hinges [authorities] of medicine, the marvelous net [rete mirabile] is made,[105] which is, according to them, of notable size extending before, behind, and on the sides.

The aforesaid veins that nourish the brain in their ascent must be sustained by some solid body such as the pericranium and dura mater because by themselves they could not ascend, on account of their simple, soft tunic.

The blood in them is also more apt to descend than to ascend because it is heavy. The arteries are not supported by any solid body, but standing by themselves they ascend to the inner part of the cranium because they have two tunics and are hard.

It was not necessary for them to ascend and afterward to turn their heads downward like veins, because their blood is light and more fitted for ascent than for descent.

You will see the branches of these veins and of some arteries better in the anatomy of the following members.

The substance of the veins and arteries has been described elsewhere. Their complexion is judged from their composition. Their form is well known. They are connected with the entire body. Their size is also well known. They are larger in one body than in another. The site of many of them often varies (and therefore, as I have said elsewhere, authors seem to be in disagreement about them). Their number is beyond perception because many of them are hidden. Their services are to feed all the members. They suffer all kinds of ills. Often there occurs in them an obstruction in drawing together caused by an excess of blood. If this happens in the branches of the guidez veins, a deep sleep always follows, then apoplexy, and then final suffocation.

This guidez vein is sometimes phlebotomized—rarely, however, in our region and in our age. Its incision helps leprosy in an early stage, and in strong quinsy [*squinantia*], in acute asthma, in constriction of breath, in hoarseness of voice due to a superabundance of blood, and in an apostema (abscess) of the lung. Incision is also employed for the purpose of evacuation and diversion in any of the preceding cases in their inception and development. This incision of the guidez veins is, however, to be made by a skilful hand with a lancet that has some obstacle near its point lest all the sides of the vein be opened, since these veins are slippery to the touch and since they are not attached to flesh as many other veins are; then also because of the soft and slippery glands that exist under these veins; finally so that the lancet may not prick a nerve or other members located there.

The manner of phlebotomizing these veins is as follows. Let the patient's lower body cavity between the ilia and hypochondria first be bound properly with a girdle. Let him hold his mouth closed as he expels air from the chest. Then let him bend his head to the side opposite the phlebotomy because in so doing the vein swells like a stretched cord. With a suitable instrument and with the vein held firmly by the hand or some other means, the vein must be perforated in its higher part. Authors recommend that such an incision should be made along the width of the vein; I should, however, cut obliquely. Do not allow a large quantity of blood to be released, nor phlebotomize a second time. Let the operator have at hand powders for coagulating the blood, such as Armenian bole, dragon's blood, rabbit hairs, mummy (otherwise pissasphalt, not dry human flesh, as more modern doctors use). frankincense bark, aloes, and so forth, and among all things let him have vitriol or colcothar. Soot is also praised for this purpose, and burned beans or paper. (Burned) skins and materials similar to them, with white of egg well beaten, should be placed on top of the incision together with a proper bandage. Let the patient lie with his head elevated for eight days, sleeping lightly and eating a proper diet, as directed by the physician in charge.

CONCERNING THE ANATOMY OF THE DESCENDING AND REVERSIVE NERVES

Having disposed of the anatomy of the veins ascending upward from the liver, as well as saying much about the ascending arteries, I return to the descending nerves,[106] from which the reversives arise.[107] I say that in the lateral parts of the neck a little below the ears, between, or rather under, some muscles, there are notable veins and arteries, as was revealed above. To these veins and arteries on both sides adheres a notable nerve, called descending. These nerves the ancients called apoplectic, but badly, because they did not recognize their operations. According to Galen in his book *On the Voice and the Breath,* these nerves arise chiefly from the sixth pair of nerves of the brain and also from the third pair.[108] They descend perpendicularly because that is the way in which they must move the members.

These nerves are composed of many branches, of which some, according to Galen, are in their descent spread to the heart,[109] to its capsule, to the mediastinus, and also to the chest in the roots of the ribs. Certain quite notable ones go to the mouth of the stomach and to the diaphragm.[110] Some smaller branches go to the liver, spleen,[111] kidneys,[112] and other members with sensation of the lower body cavities. To these members also go some nerves that descend obliquely from the nape of the neck, and from these descending nerves notable branches are once more turned upward; these are called reversive and nerves that turn back.[113] They are commonly called nerves of the voice and pass to the epiglottis, binding themselves with certain of its muscles whose heads are located near the lower parts of its body.

Of the aforesaid descending nerves, with the exception of these reversives, some branches,[114] in their descent, go also to some muscles of the epiglottis whose heads are turned toward the upper region. The reversives, as some think, with their muscles close the cymbalar cartilage [arytenoid] and the glottis. But the muscles of the descending nerves move the other cartilages and also open the cymbalar. From the seventh pair likewise and from the nape of the neck come nerves to the muscles of the epiglottis, according to Galen, which move it obliquely.

These nerves are two, one on the right, one on the left. They are, however, divided into many villi, or branches, as is evident on account of the many members to which they pass. Their size and color are evident. Their complexion and substance are like those of the other nerves. The reversives, however, are dryer and harder because they have to undergo notable and almost continuous motion especially when they close the epiglottis,[115] for the closing of which a stronger motion is required than for its opening because there are more muscles that open it than there are muscles to close it. Also the motion of the heart, the lung, and the chest opens it. Therefore, so that such nerves may be strong, nature has placed them far away from the humid brain, from which the farther they are distant the dryer they become. They pass near the heart around the artery where perhaps because of the heart's heat they acquire dryness and hardness and are turned back upward so that by drawing downward they may close the epiglottis. When these nerves are relaxed with the assistance of many other muscles, the epiglottis is opened.

Their site is at the sides of the neck, descending to the aforesaid members. But the nerves called reversive in the left part begin to turn back to the upper region when they meet the great aorta artery in a place a little above the heart where first that artery is divided into two parts and begins to be turned back through the chest to the lower members. Around this great descending branch is made the motion of attraction and relaxation of these nerves. This bifurcation of the artery is for these nerves like a wheel upon which with a cord water is drawn up from a well. This place both on the left and on the right near which these reversive nerves are moved or (to which they adhere) on which they are supported in their motion is called diablum and flexor by Galen. It is also called girgilus and bacham by some. Galen, *On the Assistance of the Parts* viii. 2, compares this reversion of the nerves to those who with horses in a field return to the road from which they came before and says it is like the turning back of something on a small wheel. In his book *On the Usefulness of the Parts* vii. 14, he says that he himself first of all found these nerves thus situated, their muscles having their heads toward the lower region.

He also says the reversion of these nerves shows the nerves arise from the brain and not from the heart, as Aristotle thought, because if the nerves arose from the heart, these reversive nerves would come from it and not from the brain, as is evident to the senses.

For these reversive nerves of the right side,[116] nature also made the girgilus, or that wheel which it made in the left side,[117] from one quite notable branch of the ascending artery slanted toward the right armpit around the upper fork of the chest of the right side; this artery goes to the right arm. With this branch nature joined other little skins existing therein so that it may be strong, because this branch is not as large as that around which the aforementioned reversive nerves of the right side are turned back.[118]

Under this branch of the right side fortified by the aforesaid skins the right-hand reversive nerves ascend through the neck. Both the right- and left-hand reversives in their ascent are implanted with many branches near the muscles of the epiglottis, as is evident to the senses. By means of these muscles they voluntarily move the epiglottis, or larynx, as a horseman who by means of bit and reins moves his horse when he wishes.

The services of the aforesaid descending nerves are to give sensation and, according to some, a certain motion to the members to which they go in their descent; on this matter comment has been made above. The service of the reversive nerves is to give voice; therefore, they are called nerves of the voice. Both the descending and reversive nerves suffer all kinds of ills. If their complexion should be notably changed, as sometimes happens in their uncovering by reason of an ulcer, especially the complexion of the descending nerves and by chance that of the reversive nerves, the voice and the other operations of the nerves are lost. If these operations are not taken away, they are at any rate diminished, and if the reversives alone are cut into completely on both sides, the voice and speech are lost.[119] If they are cut on only one side, half of these operations is injured. But if the descending nerves are cut, of which the reversives are parts, according to some, those five operations are injured of which Galen made mention in his work *On the Inner Parts* iv. 16: (1) the departure of air from the chest with difficult breathing, (2) a blast of breath without stroke or noise, (3) a blast with noise, (4) the voice, and (5) the speech. Some insist, however, that by the incision of the descending nerves the voice alone is lost as well as the blast with stroke. On these nerves see my *Commentary*.

Having seen these items, put the reversive nerves back into their place in the neck so that by means of them you may better see the muscles of the epiglottis to which they are attached. Put back also the upper part of the stomach, the entire gullet, or meri, and that upper part of the lung which you saved for viewing the trachea. Put back, too, such parts of the veins and arteries stretching to the arms and head as will enable you to see their anatomy in their place. Throw away the heart and the other members of the lower and middle body cavities which were seen first and saved for viewing the veins, arteries, and nerves mentioned earlier. Before we proceed in the present order of anatomy, something must be said about the face and about some of its parts. Then we must turn to the epiglottis and to the gullet.

CONCERNING THE FACE

That anterior part of the head which is known to all and which belongs to man alone is called facies by the Romans, prosopon by the Greeks. This part should rather be anatomized with the upper body cavity than with the middle cavity, but we shall speak of it incidentally in the present discussion because in a common anatomy the gullet, or meri (and throat), cannot be investigated unless we first make mention of some parts of the face. We say face as if it "makes" man. For by the face the recognition and distinction of each person is made.

This part called face is also called vultus [countenance], from rolling [*volvendo*] and from willing [*volendo*], because through it the affections of the mind are known, in which its color is changed either because of bashfulness or because of some crime committed or on account of fear or illness. There are some people whose countenance rarely changes, and these are called "poker-faced" [*vultuosi*].

The countenance changes from age to age. The face differs from the countenance in this respect, that the face stays always the same and the countenance is changed, although the face changes color and size according to its age. Knowledge of the face is much prized by the physiognomist. It is also prized by the physician, since you will make the first prognostication primarily from the face of the sick man; for this is helpful in the recognition of many diseases, such as leprosy, consumption, yellow jaundice, cachexia [general ill health and malnutrition], and the time of menstruation in woman. In the face are also recognized those who pretend illness, but not always.

Its site is under the anterior part of the hairy head. Its substance is of rarer, smoother skin than the skin elsewhere on the body, for the sake of vapors ascending to it from the whole body and for the sake of comeliness. There are many muscles under the skin itself, pulsating and quiet veins, nerves, panniculi, ligaments, cartilages, and bones. In number it is one organic member.

The number of its parts are forehead, temples, ears, eyebrows, the space between the eyebrows, the nose, eyes, eyelids, eyelashes, cheeks, jaws, or mandibles, which in the present context are synonymous, the mouth, the upper or puffed-out cheek, the lips, the dimples, the mustache, the cleft under the nose, and the chin with its cleft. Its size, form, and connections are evident. Its complexion is such as the complexion of its component parts. Its services are to be assumed from its parts. It suffers ills of all kinds.

CONCERNING THE FOREHEAD AND OTHER PARTS OF THE FACE, WITH THE EXCEPTION OF THE NOSE, EYES, EYELIDS, EYELASHES, AND MOUTH WITH ITS PARTS

The forehead is all that middle part at the top of the face, naked of hair, which is above the eyes; by some, nevertheless, it is said that the eyes are in the forehead, and thus, according to Varro, the forehead is so called from the boring [*foratu*] of the eyes.

Under the skin of the forehead is one dilated muscle with its villi along the length of the body with which it moves the eyebrows.[120] In the forehead also there are wrinkles stretching along its breadth according to whose location itinerant physicians cut abscesses [*exituras*], but badly, because then the eyebrows fall. Therefore, the section ought to be made in the forehead along the length of the body.

In the forehead are some veins which in different diseases are cut, and leeches are also applied to them. Under the aforesaid muscle and panniculus of the cranium is a bone of the forehead called the coronal bone.[121]

CONCERNING THE TEMPLES

At the sides of the forehead are the temples [tempora], so called because in them are recognized the years of many living creatures. For they grow grey first in men, but not always. They grow hollow also in the long duration of time. In the temples are little oblong bones stretching through the transverse direction of the head which guard the temporal muscles within themselves and the cranium. These bones are called by Avicenna the bones of the pair [ossa paris],[122] and beyond the aforesaid muscles in the temples there are also some outstanding arteries and veins which in some diseases are cut.[123]

CONCERNING THE SUPERCILIA, OR EYEBROWS

The eyebrows are known to all. Their site is at the end of the forehead. They are born with man for the sake of ornament, intended by nature to guard the eyes from falling dust, from rain, and similar things. Their hairs do not grow as those of the head, for the sake of a good end [purpose].

OF THE SPACE BETWEEN THE EYEBROWS

In the confines of the forehead is a certain space which divides the eyebrows in their middle.[124] It also divides the forehead from the nose and lower and middle parts of the forehead conterminous with this part as to a center. This place is called glabella or glabra. For glaber means "without hairs"; this place is also called the comeliness of the nose [*lepor nasi*]. In this place erysipelas often begins, which is called by another name by modern physicians, rosy drop [gutta rosea].

CONCERNING THE CHEEKS

The cheeks are those round parts in the face which are also called apples. They are below the eyes at the sides of the nose and exist in man alone. They are properly called genae, although the greater part of the face is named gena. The skin of this part is thinner than that in any other part of the face; it easily grows red and changes its natural color through affections of the mind. This color is commonly rosy in those of good complexion. These cheeks adorn the face and are a protection to the eyes and nose. Each of them has one broad muscle very firmly united to its skin which serves them and the lips,[125] as shall be told later in the section of the lips.

CONCERNING THE BEARD, CALLED GENA

In the face there is also a bearded part which has its proper name and is called gena from the Greek *genao* [Latin, *genero*], "to beget," because there the hairs are generated. This part is also called by some mistax or mustax [mustache].

CONCERNING THE CHIN

In the lower part of the face is the chin [mentum], so called from its appearance above the rest [*eminendo*]. It is also called anthereon. It stands out above the gullet. Its disease is called mentagra, from mentum. Its highest part begins from the root of the upper lip, and it has its terminus in the lowest part of the face. Because of such a location it can be called mentum, because the lowest in all things, if not meek [*mites*], ought to be meek.

In the middle of the chin is a certain hollow called by some buccula and bucella, a little cheek; it is also called the typos.

CONCERNING THE DIMPLES

On both sides of the mouth in the skin in some individuals, especially in boys and women, there is a certain little pit which appears in laughter. This indicates grace and charm. Therefore such little pits are called the navel of Venus and dimple. They are called the navel of Venus because they resemble the hollow found in the leaves of that herb which is called Venus' navel and cotyledon.

CONCERNING THE CLEFT UNDER THE NOSE

Under the nose in the middle of the lower lip is a certain little valley which Lactantius Firmianus called a ditch because of its resemblance to a hollow. By some it is called philtron, spherion, and hispia. The nose, eyes, eyelids, eyelashes, mouth, and their parts will be discussed in their place, beginning with the anatomy of the mouth.

CONCERNING THE ANATOMY OF THE MOUTH AND ITS PARTS

In order that the trachea, epiglottis, and gullet may be investigated comfortably as I promised, I turn to the dissection of the mouth and its parts, and I say that the mouth is that hollow part in the face immediately inside the lips through which first the food and drink and in part the air enter the body, and through which issue the saliva and voices and in which speech is made. The mouth is so called [os] as if it were a door [ostium] for putting the food and drink in and out.

The cheek or cheeks are those parts in the face or mouth which can be naturally inflated with the breath, that is, the cavity itself of the mouth which is inflated by breath called back from the lung and retained in the mouth while the lips are compressed.

The parts of the mouth are lips, teeth, gums, jaws, palate, uvula, tongue, tonsils, and the upper part of the throat.

From what has been said, the substance, site, and form of the mouth are evident. Its size is well known to all. It is a single member. The number of its parts has been told. Its connections are assumed from its parts and likewise for its services. Its complexion is the same as that of its parts. It suffers all kinds of ills.

CONCERNING THE LIPS

The lips [labia], which are also called labra, are thick in some people, thin in others. Thick lips commonly indicate a rudeness of character. The prominent part of the lips is named prochilus. Their continual coming together is called prostomion or prostomia, and those in whom the lips and teeth are prominent are called brochi. In the middle of the lips is a fissure which is properly called the mouth.

The substance of the lips is composed of muscular flesh,[126] skin, and a panniculus continuous with the gullet. The union of these parts is so compact that with the greatest difficulty can one be separated from another. It is such so that their agile motion may not be impeded by their thickness. This motion serves for every difference of position. Therefore there are four muscles proper to the lips and two muscles common to them and to the cheekballs.[127]

The proper muscles are small in proportion to the lips. They are bound together with each other before they are united to the skin in such a way that their parts are inseparable without lacerating them. One pair of these muscles hangs under the cheek balls obliquely toward the lips.[128] The other two hang obliquely from the lower jaw toward the lips.[129]

Although there are only four muscles for the lips, they have nevertheless eight movements, according to Galen, *On the Usefulness of the Parts* xi. 16, that is, four straight and four oblique. Each one of these, while it is moved, moves obliquely because the site of each of them is oblique. But when two of them are moved equally, they move straightly, as in the opening of the lips in which there is one straight movement. Another straight movement in the lips occurs when they are closed together or compressed.

There are two other straight movements in the lips. One occurs when they are turned outward and the other when they are folded inward. These movements are made by the straight villi or fibers, of which some are intrinsic to the same muscles of the lips and some extrinsic. When the extrinsic villi are stretched, then the lips are turned outward; when the intrinsic are stretched, then the lips are folded under or inward. How the oblique movements are made by one muscle and the straight movements by more than one muscle is easy to judge if you examine the closings of a purse. When they are drawn together straightly and uniformly they open the mouth of the purse, and when one closing is drawn, the mouth of the purse is moved transversely.

Avicenna, however, although he speaks of the aforesaid site of the muscles, sets down only four movements, just as there are four muscles. He says four movements are enough for them. He further declares that one part of them, when it is moved, moves to its part; when two are moved to two parts, they are dilated to two parts. Therefore they have a complementary movement to four parts, nor do they have any other movement except these.

Both Galen and Avicenna speak of the proper motion of the lips because there is a motion common to cheeks and lips made by two broad muscles in each mandible.[130] The broad muscles are larger than those described before. Those, according to Galen, are outward from the cheeks to the spine of the neck. To these muscles come nerves from the chest and from the clavicles,[131] that is, from the upper forks of the chest, which are implanted in the cheeks and lower lip by straight villi. Some other villi stretching obliquely also from the clavicles and some others more oblique than the aforesaid ascending from the shoulder blades along the sides of the lips are implanted in the cheeks. Still others stretch to these muscles from the place behind the ears,[132] which they sometimes move. These muscles are not clearly recognized although they have a multitude of nerves from almost all parts of the neck. They are recognized, however, if with closed jaws the lips and the cheekballs are moved to their utmost power, not because the bony parts of the cheekballs are moved but because their fleshy muscular part mentioned before is moved with the skin, which is properly for the sole motion of the lips. To this part and to the lips themselves go the aforesaid broad muscles which move the lips and cheeks. This is called the common motion, that is, of lips and cheekballs.

Some also insist that the cheekballs in their upper part are moved somewhat by the broad muscle that moves the forehead, and some say that those broad muscles that move the cheekballs and lips also assist mastication.

The motion of these muscles is best seen in living bodies, especially in those who are quite thin. Therefore I shall make mention of them, omitting the anatomy of many muscles since they cannot be seen in living bodies nor pointed out in common anatomy. I shall describe the muscles of the tongue and of the jaws for the same reason.

The lips within themselves and also the entire mouth are covered with a panniculus that covers the gullet, or meri, and the stomach as well, and because of this the lower lip trembles when one is about to vomit. This panniculus is harder and thicker in the mouth than elsewhere and thicker in the meri than in the stomach. In its descent it is made ever smoother and thinner because in the mouth it first meets the food that is rather hard and which is made softer as it descends. Galen, *On the Usefulness of the Parts* iv, and along with this passage Avicenna both believe that that which nourishes receives some digestion by mastication.

The form, site, size, and number of the lips are evident. Their complexion is set down as warm; they are connected with the brain by nerves, with the liver by veins, with the heart by arteries, and therefore in their compression are discovered the affections of the mind. The lips are also stretched and compressed voluntarily. They are connected with the stomach, meri, and with the whole body by means of the skin. Their services are many—for guarding the teeth, for the good form of the face, for the expression of speech, for taking food and drink—and they are for the mouth like a house door, opening and closing themselves when necessary. They prevent the cold air from entering the heart by itself and by accident. They also retain the air called back from the lung in necessity.

The lips suffer all kinds of ills, chapping [rhagades] among others. They often suffer from cancer, trembling in crises and in fevers through communication from the brain and from the stomach.

CONCERNING THE TEETH

Having seen the foregoing, first open the mouth as far as you can, cutting the cheeks on both sides so that you may better see the teeth and gums, first noting the substance of the teeth which is bony and, according to Celsus, harder than bone. Some say, however, that the teeth are of the nature of flesh and of bone because they both feel and grow again. They also increase for the sake of their purpose throughout the whole time of their permanence, since if they did not increase they would not endure, and mastication would be bad; hence life would be short.

There are thirty-two of them, sixteen in a row along both cheeks. There are often only twenty-eight because the four back teeth are missing. These are called neguegid by Avicenna; there are two on each side. Sometimes six in all are lacking. The neguegid are the last to grow; they are called the teeth of the intellect, the sense, and wisdom because in some people they come forth in manhood or old age. According to Aristotle, *On the Nature or History of Animals* ii, there are more teeth in males than in females, as is evident in the races of humans, sheep, pigs, and goats.

Their names are variously given by Celsus, Galen, Aristotle, Avicenna, and Mundinus. These are, first, the names of the teeth as given by Avicenna, in every part, whether upper or lower, from the middle of the mouth toward the front. Beginning in the middle there are first two quite broad equal teeth called duals;[133] at the sides of these on both sides there is one called incisives by Mundinus and quadrupli by Avicenna.[134] Galen, however, calls the duals incisives. These two duals and two incisives Celsus calls quaterni. Aristotle calls all of these acute, insofar as they cut, and agrees with Galen. On both sides of these there is one tooth commonly called cynodentes or canines; by some they are called dimple teeth [*gelasini*] because they appear more in laughter than the rest.

Then there are according to Avicenna all the molars,[135] so called from grinding [*molendo*]. According to him, in some people there are four molars on both sides of the canine teeth; in some people there are five, and in this way there are thirty-two or twenty-eight teeth, numbering two duals, two quadrupli or incisives, and two canines, six all together. The molars, according to Avicenna, are ten or eight. That is, if there are ten in each part, upper or lower, there are sixteen in all, and thus there are a total of thirty-two. But if there are eight in each part, then there are fourteen in all and a total of twenty-eight.

Mundinus includes in the number thirty-two—two duals above and two below, two incisives, two canines, four molars, and six maxillars. Neither Galen nor Aristotle gives particular names to all the teeth, but Celsus reckons four canines, two on each side next to the quaterni above and the same number below; he also reckons eight maxillars above and eight below, that is, four on both sides next to the canines.

Their form is diverse, for some have one single sharp head and one root, as all the duals, quadruples, or incisives, and canines have. The lower molars have at least two heads and two roots, and sometimes three and the same number of heads, especially the farthest teeth. The upper teeth have at least three heads and as many roots and sometimes four, especially the farthest which are like a wall that holds the others firm. The roots of the upper teeth are curved in order to be more firm so that they may not fall with their weight; they also have foramina in which they are fixed; these are marvelously adapted to them.

From the jawbone arises for each tooth one round addition that fastens the tooth by means of strong ligaments.[136] Galen calls these additions presepia, mangers; not only are they in the place of the gums, but they are also at the end of the roots of the teeth.

The molars have more roots than the others because their operation is more continuous than that of the other teeth and because in mastication they are moved not upward and downward alone but also sideways or circularly.

All the teeth, according to Galen and Avicenna, have some sensation.

Their size and site are evident. They are connected with the jaws and gums and with the brain by a nerve. Their complexion is well known. Their service is to prepare food for the stomach; they also modulate the speech. They are also the weapons of nature.

They suffer all manner of ills which other bones suffer. Pain is felt in them; they also suffer commotion, corrosion, putrefaction, congealing, alteration of color, and elongation from their natural place.

CONCERNING THE GUMS

After the teeth, the gums [gingivae] are to be examined. They are so called from their creation of teeth [a gignendis dentibus]. They are of simple flesh, and hard. In them are fixed the teeth. In them also are as many foramina as there are teeth.

There are two of them, one above, the other below. Their form is evident; it follows the form of the jaw. Their site is also evident as well as their size and connections. Their services are to strengthen the teeth, to clothe the jawbones near the teeth, to comfort those bones with their warmth, and to offer those who have no teeth the service of mastication. They have considerable feeling owing to their connection with the brain by means of nerves dispersed among them.[137] They suffer all sorts of ills.

CONCERNING THE PALATE

After the gums, according to the true method of universal anatomy, comes the palate,[138] which is part of the mouth according to Aristotle, *On the History of Animals* i. 11; it is that part in the mouth, open or closed, which is above the tongue.

This part is bony and composed of the bones of the upper jaws. It is nevertheless protected with some flesh and covered by its panniculus, which has some nerves in it that give the sensation of taste (and of touch).[139] This part in the mouth is similar to the hollow of a tortoise shell or the vault of a furnace. Therefore it is called caelum [vault of the sky] or altum [height]. It is called the palate because in the opening of the mouth it is plainly [palam] revealed to us and because it clearly seems broad [latum]. The palate, according to Galen, is, as it were, the bell lying in front of the larynx or epiglottis, in which the intonation of the voice is made (and the notable sense of taste by means of nerves).

Its site, form, size, number, and connections are evident. Its complexion is cold because it is predominantly bony. In this member there is no foramen serving the pituitary body [colatorium], as some think, through which the superfluities of the brain are drained away, but such a foramen or foramina exist in the basilar bone above the nostrils, as will be said elsewhere.

Its service is to retain air in the mouth, whether closed or open, in order to warm the air if it is cold so that it may not injure the heart by reaching it in that condition. It also retains the air by which the heart is refreshed in necessity. It also assists in retaining the vocal air, and therefore the palate is wrinkled so that the air may escape in waves. The palate with its hollow also assists the revolution of the food in the mouth during mastication. Also by means of its concavity the tongue is more agilely moved for its operations. With its skin it assists digestion, the skin of the entire mouth participating in this assistance, with the saliva perhaps mixed with the food in mastication.

It suffers ills of all sorts. Among other diseases it suffers cola or alcola in fevers.

CONCERNING THE UVULA, OR UVEA

At the end of the palate near the upper throat toward the head just opposite the root of the tongue is a fleshy member of thin substance covered with membrane whose size and form are comparable to a grapeseed and which is therefore called uva, uvigena, and uvigera. It is also called columella, columna, and by some gargareon, gargar, gurgulio, and fundibulum. This member grows beyond nature in length and width when humidity fills it, and sometimes it looks like a mouse's tail, as I have often seen it. Sometimes it grows hard and sometimes strangles one, according to Aristotle.

This member exists in man only.[140] Its substance has been described; there are in it some veins and arteries,[141] and therefore if it is severely injured, it draws the blood. Its complexion is warm and humid. Its number, site, and connections are evident. This member gives way to things that are swallowed; it does not have voluntary movement. Therefore it lacks muscles.[142] It assists in breaking up and altering the air and, according to some, in modulating the voice. It also prevents thirst by preventing air from violently entering the upper throat.

It suffers all kinds of ills, especially corrosion and softening, in which cautery is often required.

CONCERNING THE TONGUE

The tongue is sometimes taken for the variety of languages, as Greek, Arab, Latin, and so forth. It also signifies many other things. In the present context it is understood to mean the member contained in the mouth. Tongue [lingua] is so called from binding [ligando] because it is bound from one end of the mouth to the other within the lower jaws.

The substance of this member is naturally thin, fungous, and soft. It is accidentally soft because of the humidities descending to it from the head and from the stomach. The glandulous flesh in its root in which there are fountains of saliva moistens it by means of saliva. The tongue also has a multitude of nerves,[143] both for the senses of touch and taste as well as for movement. The nerves which give taste come from the third pair of nerves of the brain. Those which give motion come from the seventh pair; these nerves are notable because the tongue requires excellent feeling and motion as well as a great deal of heat and nourishment. Therefore, like the penis, it has more and larger pulsating and quiet veins than any other member equal to it in size.[144] The nerves which give it motion are distinct from those which give sensation, but those which give the sense of touch give also taste,[145] and taste is easily corrupted by touch because taste is a more subtle virtue than touch. The site of the nerves of sensation is superficial. The site of the nerves of motion is nearer the center more or less according to the location of the muscles, which are commonly reckoned as nine,[146] that is, four pairs and one solitary, by which the tongue is moved to every difference of position. The tongue at its root is wide, thick, and strong. In its anterior part it is thin and sharp to be more ready for movement.

Of the aforesaid muscles, two are on the sides of the tongue, one on each side; these are called the latitudinal muscles and proceed from the sharp bones of the head placed behind the ears.[147] From this place also in part come the villi of one (that) muscle which is common for the motion of the lips and for the motion of the cheekballs of the face.[148] These bones are called sagittalia and acularia,[149] arrow bones and needle bones. There are also two muscles called longitudinal originating from the top of the lambda bone which are continued with the middle of the tongue. There are two other muscles which move the tongue transversely; these proceed from the side which is the lower of the two sides of the lambda bone. These muscles penetrate between the aforesaid longitudinal and latitudinal muscles.

There are two other muscles which turn the tongue around and turn it upward. The villi of these muscles are spread in the width under the aforesaid muscles and are continuous with the bone of the lower jaw. Avicenna, however, in his book on *Animals* xii, says these last muscles are above the others. Then there is one muscle called the solitary which continues the tongue to the lambda bone and draws one to the other. This muscle drives the tongue to the outer parts and lengthens it; it also draws the tongue back and shortens it.

There are many who say the tongue is not moved outward voluntarily but merely involuntarily by the imagination, like the penis. Some say both the tongue and the penis are moved by muscles and by the imagination at the same time. Some say it is moved by the imagination alone, which by means of the spirit causes a windiness that dilates and erects the penis and likewise the tongue, bringing it out of the mouth. These matters are handled by Galen, *On the Motions of Liquids* i, and by Avicenna, in the first of the first book [*Canon*] in the chapter on the muscles of the tongue. There the commentators resolve doubts: look them up.

CONCERNING THE BONES OF THE TONGUE

The tongue at its roots has a bone to which it is knit and fastened and made firm as upon its basis in many of its movements.[150] This bone is quadrilateral and not very hard but, as it were, cartilaginous. It is called the hyoid bone and lambda, or lambe, because it resembles that Greek letter. Two of its (smaller) sides are toward the tongue; these are bifurcated in the form of the letter mentioned. The two other sides are similarly formed, larger than the first two. They are toward the peltal or shield-shaped cartilage of the epiglottis which they embrace and to which they are bound so that it may not slide this way or that and so that this bone may better make firm the other members fastened to it. This bone is fastened not only to the epiglottis but also to the meri by some ligaments.[151] (This bone, however, in man rarely has four sides, but two only toward the epiglottis.)

This bone was not made in an oblong or straight form, because the weight of the tongue would have drawn it to one side only and there would then have been no good speech or mastication. This bone is called the hyoid by Galen, and lambda bone; Avicenna calls it alfahic.

The services of this bone are set down as many by Galen, although it is a little bone. First, many muscles come from it to the tongue,[152] and some muscles of the epiglottis,[153] some to the shoulder blades,[154] some to the chest,[155] and some to the jaws.[156] From it also or from its ligaments arise the tendons of the muscles near to it. It is a defense of the shield cartilage of the larynx (epiglottis). This bone is the principal foundation upon which the tongue is turned in its movements.

This bone has three conjugations of muscles proper to it. One pair proceeds from the extremities of the lower jaw toward that part with which it is continued to the root of the tongue.[157] One of these muscles is at the right, the other at the left. When this pair is contracted, it draws the tongue toward the jaw.

The second pair arises under the chin and passes to that [hyoid] bone under the tongue and is attached to it toward the upper part, that is, toward the epiglottis; and it draws this bone to the part or direction of the jaw.[158]

The third pair arises from the needle-like additions of the bone of the head, that is, from the two sharp bony extremities behind the ears.[159] These muscles are continued with the extremity of this bone, which is turned toward the tongue, and they draw it upward toward the posterior part.

All the other muscles continued to this bone are common to it and to the members to which they pass.

Under the tongue are two notable veins,[160] one on each side. They are phlebotomized in many states of ill health, especially in synanche [quinsy];

they are red, sometimes black, and sometimes green, and are called by some raninae, pertaining to a frog.

Also under the tongue where it is attached to the mouth are certain notable bipartite caverns which are called orifices or mouths or fountains of saliva.[161] These are called by Avicenna the generators of saliva; into them a stylus easily enters. These orifices are opened and closed like a purse as the saliva increases and decreases. These fountains terminate at the aforesaid glandulous flesh located in the root of the tongue,[162] from which continually a salivary humidity sweats out into the fountains just mentioned.

Under the tongue there is a certain little skin in the middle extending through its length which is called by our Italians "the little thread." This is large in some people, and midwives or surgeons cut it in infancy. If they do not cut it, this little skin makes the child tongue-tied or hard of speech.

The complexion of the tongue is warm and humid. Its form, site, and connections are evident from what has been said. Its size is conspicuous. According to Aristotle, one tongue is broad, another narrow, another small, but that tongue is praiseworthy which is measured in its length and width according to its power of speech.

One may see that it is one in number. Although there are two members, they appear one member composed of two similar ones. Nature has commonly created double senses so that if harm comes to one part, the other part remains unharmed. It was not perceptibly to the senses divided into two parts distant from each other for mastication and speech but was united by means of a panniculus that covers it. This panniculus is divided lengthwise into two sides above and below; but it is united and very firmly bound to the tongue. This panniculus is continuous with the panniculus that covers the stomach and meri and all the inner part of the mouth.[163]

The services of the tongue are primarily for the distinction of the voice and for articulating the letters of words. Therefore Galen, in *On the Voice and Breath,* said that for voice and speech three members are assigned—the trachea, epiglottis, and tongue. Each of these has glands which temper it with moisture (which impart moisture to them).

The glands of the trachea which moisten it are in the neck,[164] and they make the parts of the neck equal.

The glands of the epiglottis are those which are called chests of air, arcae aeris.

A certain fat glandulous flesh near that covering of the epiglottis is called glottis. This is a principal organ of voice. The tongue has glands also to which veins pass carrying saliva to them; the rest [of the glands] lack a vein but by their own nature are filled with humidity flowing to them from above and below. In the epiglottis is generated the humidity with which it is moistened. Some humidity flows to it also from the head.

The tongue also assists in the differentiation of taste, in the revolution of the food in the mouth so that every part of it is ground up, and in swallowing. It suffers ills of all kinds.

CONCERNING THE TONSILS

In the upper lateral part of the tongue near its root there are certain adenous or glandulous pieces of flesh, one on each side, called almonds [*amigdala, tonsils*] by many. These, together with the uvea aforementioned and the galsamac and alfahic, are placed by Avicenna [*Canon*], ix. 3, among the parts added to the throat. The interpreter of Avicenna understands by throat that space in which are the passageways of the food and breath, but badly, because throat [guttur] commonly is taken by the Latins for the trachea artery. It is taken also for the anterior part of the neck, which extends from the upper part of the throat [fauces] to the iugulum. Therefore Celsus said the granges veins, that is, guidez, are at the right and left near the throat. According to Pliny, the throat is so large in man that it often swells in illness; this tumor or swelling is called botium and also struma, although struma also indicates scrofula and some other tumors.

Therefore this space behind the uvea and the aforesaid tonsils and the galsamac and alfahic is called faux. Faux or guttur in the method of Avicenna [*Canon*], ix. 3, is not any member at all but is that vacuity at which the top of the gullet, or meri (and trachea), terminates and in whose contermination toward the front part are the uvea, tonsils, alfahic, and galsamac. In its upper termination is that vacuity which terminates above the palate at the nose and at the basilar bone toward the turnings [anfractus] that exist under the pituitary body. We shall speak of these parts later. The neck is also called faux by the interpreter of Galen, *On the Voice and Breath* i. (I call neck that place which is between the upper part of the epiglottis and the upper part of oesophagus as far as the root of the tongue. The interpreter, however, says that in this place are the muscles of the bronchi.)

The aforesaid glands of which we intend to speak at present are commonly called tonsils. Celsus calls them glands, and Mundinus calls them fauces, although incorrectly; the Greeks call them antiades and paristhmia.

The substance of these tonsils is fleshy and sinewy, that is, fitted with little skins by which it is attached laterally coming from the root of the tongue toward the palate,[165] and by means of these little skins the aforesaid tonsils are united to the palate. These sinewy little skins together with the glands are like cavernous auricles. Therefore they are called arca, the repository of the air.[166] These chests are notable in the dog-faced baboon; in them the baboon keeps not only air but sometimes, as I have seen, food such as chestnuts, chick-peas, hazel nuts, beans, and similar items. These tonsils with their little skins are seen better in one individual than in another and better in a live creature because in a dead one they are drawn back. These chests keep the air more in its exit than in its entrance so that all of it does not go forth from the way of the heart and the creature perish, so that in submersion in water and in [the holding of the breath] stinks it may be restored by this retained air.

These little skins alone, according to some, are those which Avicenna calls galsamac or golzama, but in my judgment they are nothing but the afore-said chests, because Avicenna says that above galsamac is alfahic, that is, the lambda bone. This bone is annexed to the tongue and epiglottis in front, under these little skins. If these little skins are golzama or galsamac, then the text of Avicenna is corrupt, that is, where he says, "And alfahic is above galsamac." There is no other member in that place toward the palate except the uvea and the little skins of the glands, which our discussion has passed by, which make a chest for the retention of air. Therefore galsamac is not in that place, but in my judgment galsamac is (the tongue of the fistula called) the epiglottis, that is, that covering of skin which closes the epiglottis lest food and other extraneous materials enter it, as we shall explain later on.

From what has been said, the services of the tonsils are apparent. Apparent also are their connections, form, size, and number. Their site is best seen when the tongue is depressed and the mouth open to its fullest extent. Their complexion is warm and moist.

They suffer all kinds of ills. At the present day in a certain endemic (epi-demic) disease vulgarly called the French sickness [syphilis] the tonsils suffer apostema, induration, and ulceration. They easily receive discharges [rheumata] from the head. In them is caused false squinantia [quinsy] or synanche, called branconcellus. Therefore it is said: if catarrh comes to the throat, it is called branchus; if catarrh comes to the nose, it is called coryza. They are also called dragonzellus and perhaps corruptly. At Bologna (by the people) they are called strangogioni because the tonsils are apt to strangle a person. They are also called gaioni.

You will better see these tonsils and also the tongue when the jaws are skinned in the manner which will be later described, because I shall set forth the anatomy of their muscles and of the members of the entire face and of the entire cane of the lung so that they may be seen at the will of the operator, since they are rarely demonstrated in a common dissection.

CONCERNING THE MANDIBLES, OR LOWER JAWS

Having viewed the tonsils, I have decided to describe the two lower jaws so that the rest of the neck may more comfortably and carefully be anatomized. The upper jaws will be discussed in their place. At present I take the jaws for those bones of the head in which the teeth are fixed.

First must be noted the skin which covers their muscles. This in men is commonly full of hairs. After the skin come the jaw muscles,[167] which serve three motions, that is, the motion of opening the mouth, of closing it, and of masticating and grinding. The motion of opening makes the lower jaws descend; the closing motion elevates them; the grinding motion makes them go round and round and to decline to both sides. Therefore it is necessary that the motion of closing should be made by muscles that descend from above and draw upward; the motion of opening is made in the contrary manner and that of grinding by transversion.

The closing muscles are two, large and with big tendons. They are called the temporal muscles because they are attached to the temples between the cranium and the ossa paris; in man they are small so that they may not weigh down the head and also because man does not masticate very hard foods. These muscles have large tendons terminating at the lower extremity of the jaws. They are very soft because they are near the brain, from which they receive three nerves—two from the third pair,[168] one from the fourth pair.[169] Consequently their damage is very serious. Therefore Galen, *On the Usefulness of the Parts* xi. 3, says, "If, therefore, as Hippocrates said, parts which are near, common, and prime are especially malignant [subject to illness], and there is no part nearer than the temporal muscles nor does any muscle communicate more with the brain by more nerves, it is reasonable to pay heed to the beginning of their illness." Because of their nobility nature located them in the cave of the temples between the bones that guard them on all sides. The muscles of the eyes are also very noble because they are near the brain, but they do not have as many nerves as these temporal muscles.[170] These two temporal muscles are assisted by two other muscles which pass through the inner part of the cheek to the aforesaid jaws.[171] The tendons of these temporal muscles arise not from the extremity of the muscle but from its middle, so that they may be stronger.

The muscles that open the jaws arise from the place called in Arabic alhiliricti, which are two bones called sharp, needle and arrow bones added to the occiput.[172] These bones are behind the ears, and these two muscles descending are united and form one muscle. Afterward they are separated and from them a tendon is made so that they may be strong. Then they are once more divided into branches, filled with flesh, and the muscle is made. Then it meets the bending back of the jaws, and, when it is contracted, it draws the jaw backward. Because the jaws are heavy, descending by themselves, two muscles are sufficient for them.

The masticatory muscles are two, one on each side.[173] They are triangulated and very sinewy under the cheekballs. They are of such a sort that in contraction they have diverse motions so that by their work grinding and mastication may be completed. These muscles with one base are near the ossa paris and with another base they are toward the cheekballs of the face and with another base toward the jaws. Each angle of the aforesaid muscles is very firmly mixed with that part of the face directly opposite them so that they may move the jaws in different directions. Some have insisted, according to Galen, that each of these muscles was three muscles and that the plumpness [*carnositas*] around the cheekballs of the face is in part from these muscles.

The tongue in addition to these muscles assists mastication by rolling the food around.

The muscles which elevate the jaws are large because they have a large motion and are soft because they are near the brain.

The muscles that depress the jaws are small because it is easier to depress than to elevate them and to keep them elevated.

The masticatory muscles are of medium size because the turning about of the jaws is easier than their elevation and more difficult than their depression.

Someone will marvel that nature has made the teeth of mastication larger and more numerous than those of incision. It must be said that nature prepared not only the teeth for incision of food but ordered the reason and art which she uses for cutting food. She also made the teeth of mastication larger and more numerous because the act of mastication is stronger and more permanent. For the most part, except by accident perhaps in the sick, art does not carry out the mastication as she does the incision of food.

Having viewed the muscles, so that you may better see the lambda bone and the head of the meri and the epiglottis, you will cut the skin and the aforesaid muscles toward the ears from each angle of that fissure which is called the mouth. In this section, if you can, look carefully at the aforesaid muscles and the other parts of the face, except the nose, eyelids, eyes, and ears (which will be discussed in their place), taking the skin off of them carefully. When you have seen these items, you will lay bare the bones of the lower jaws from their upper junctures to the middle of the chin in which they are very firmly united by means of one juncture. The aforesaid bones are united to the head on both sides by one loose juncture near the ears. You will note also their site, number, form, connections, and size. Their substance, complexion, and services are evident. They suffer ills of all sorts.

CONCERNING THE ANATOMY OF THE THROAT AND GULLET

Having seen the jaws, with a curved knife, saw, or other instrument move them completely from their place so that you may better see the throat and gullet.[174] Save the tongue uninjured and the lambda bone so that you may see the connections of these members with the jaws when removed. Investigate the site of the throat, gullet, and lambda bone, which is located near the root of the tongue, and the head of the throat. You should not remove these members before you see their muscles, but before you see the latter, you should take time to see the anatomy of the throat and gullet. For these members are so bound within one another by panniculi and ligaments that one cannot be investigated without the other.

The throat (or the way of the air) as it hangs under the jaws as far as the lung holds an anterior position, first, so that with its hardness it may guard the gullet and, second, because through this site there is a more direct route to the lung and thus the throat better and more easily serves it. Third, it holds an anterior position because the gullet is longer than the throat; if it were in front of the throat, either it would be slanted from the end of the throat to the stomach and swallowing would be bad or from the end of the throat to the stomach toward the back there would be some inconvenient hollowness.

The throat is an oblong body, round and hollow as a cane. Its substance is composed of many annular cartilages. They are, however, imperfect circles like those bracelets called armillae and resemble the letter C. Therefore they are called C-form cartilages and semicircular. They are larger than a semicircle, and in the part not circular they meet the gullet by means of a smooth panniculus, somewhat hard, perfectly spherical, covering and fastening the cartilages inside and out. Beyond the panniculus that covers the inner part of the throat from top to bottom, there are other ligaments that fill the throat toward the gullet where the cartilages are incomplete. These cartilages without the panniculus are properly an instrument of the voice.

The upper part of the throat is commonly called epiglottis, larynx, node of the throat, and sometimes gurgulio, bronchii, and head of the throat. The rest of the throat is often called (a trachea), an artery, a fistula or pipe of the breath, a vocal artery, rough artery, cane of the lung, and pharynx— from splitting voices [a findendis vocibus] (as some choose to think) or from speaking [fando]—gargar, and gargareon. It is called larynx for the most part by the interpreter of Galen, On the Usefulness of the Parts, in Latin. The larynx is taken for the upper part of itself, but commonly the lower part is called trachea and throat from garriendo, because garritus, chattering, comes from there. Avicenna in the chapter on the muscles of the throat, i. 1, understands this member as the throat, but in ix. 3 he takes as throat that space behind the palate in which there is the passage for food and breath that the Latins call faux or fauces.

This member is also called bronchium or bronchum from its resemblance to a certain fish of that name and also to an earthworm called bronchium whose body is oblong, cartilaginous or scaly, and annular like a snake.

The lowest portion of this member is divided into two parts, one on the right, the other on the left which enters the upper part of the lung, from here ever diminishing through the entire substance of the lung, through its center to the extremities divided into infinite fibers throughout the lung, carrying and recarrying the spirit to the heart in the manner revealed in our investigation of the lung.

This member is formed not from a single cartilage but from many, convex on the outside and concave on the inside, united one near the other with some distance between by ligaments and panniculi so that by means of the villi of the panniculi which are longitudinal and by means of the nerves of their muscles this member can be extended and drawn back in its movements. It is moderately hard and light so that it can be sonorous, and it is deprived of sensation so that it may resist external injuries. It is spherical because it is less liable thus to be injured. Its cartilages toward the gullet are incomplete so that with their hardness they may resist what is swallowed. Therefore the channel of the trachea is filled behind by the aforesaid ligaments and panniculi which with their softness yield to what is swallowed. Because of this in necessities the hollow of the throat within, its panniculi giving way, serves the gullet when great mouthfuls are being swallowed. The panniculi of the throat easily obey in swallowings because the time of breathing and of swallowing is different. Not only does the throat serve the gullet in this, but the gullet serves the throat in breathing. At the time of breathing the gullet is empty, as the throat is empty of breath at the time of swallowing, since in swallowings the epiglottis is always closed.

The posterior part of the throat is not cartilaginous but is pannicular so that it can be moistened more easily by drink or by licking up something wet with the tongue, as often happens in great heats and fevers, and so that more easily by hawking any material contained in the chest may be brought forth, just as is shown in the illness of pleurisy.

This member was wisely mixed of cartilage and skin for two reasons, that is, the sound, or voice, and breathing. It serves the latter and the voice, but it is not sonorous toward the gullet, because there it is smooth and almost fleshy. Therefore if the trachea and epiglottis are not properly dry but humid, hoarseness is created, according to Galen, *On the Voice and Breath,* as is the case before drinking or taking liquid food when the voice is clear and sonorous. When drink is taken and the gullet moistens the trachea very near and united to it, a clear voice is not given forth; and if the trachea is excessively moistened with drink or discharge [rheumate], hoarseness is created. Thus old men are hoarse because of the moistness of these parts. Dry bodies have a clearer and more sonorous voice than humid bodies. If the instruments of the passages of voice are opened, then suddenly much air comes forth, and this is breathing. If the instruments are contracted, there is something audible with the breathing, different according to the difference of the instrument contracted. If the epiglottis is contracted, the voice is made; if only the cane of the throat is contracted, some sound will be made which is between breathing and voice. This is hoarseness. So says Galen.

From that which has been said, the substance of the throat is evident. Its lower (inner) panniculus is quite solid and hard to resist catarrhs, evil hawkings, and the smoky vapor breathed back from the heart and to resist the movements of the throat in making the voice. The site, form, connections, number, and services of the throat as well as its size are conspicuous. Its complexion is cold and dry. It suffers ills of all sorts.

CONCERNING THE HEAD OF THE THROAT, WHICH IS CALLED EPIGLOTTIS

Having viewed the foregoing, I come to the uppermost part of the throat. The principal substance of this member is made from many cartilages joined to each other with great skill and care.[175] From these the voice and the conservation of life result [*conservatio* in the text; but did B. intend to write *conversatio,* conversation?]. The muscles, ligaments, and panniculi covering the entire trachea inside and out bind these cartilages together.

This member, according to Galen, is made not from a single cartilage but from many cartilages dissimilar in form and size, so that it can be dilated by benefit of their number and contracted for breathing and voice. It has at least four cartilages, one of which is not pure cartilage. Therefore authors commonly reckon three pure cartilages in the epiglottis. The first pure cartilage is called peltal or scutal or shield-shaped because it has the form of a shield.[176] Its convex side is toward the front; the concave side is turned toward the center of the epiglottis to the passage of air. This cartilage is larger than the others, and we can see it sticking out prominently in the anterior part of the neck beneath the skin.

After the scutal cartilage toward the gullet, or meri, is the second pure cartilage,[177] which lacks a name and has no name from the Greeks or Latins. Therefore it is called the nameless cartilage or the one that has no name. This second cartilage has its lower part in the form of a perfect circle; with this lower part it is united in back, front, and sides to the highest ring of the trachea artery. Toward the front it is firmly united with its circular part under the scutal cartilage. The scutal cartilage has two notable additions with which it embraces the second cartilage.[178] These two cartilages united compose the entire circular pore or duct of air in front, behind, and on the sides, completely cartilaginous and hard.

The third pure cartilage is commonly called cymbalaris,[179] and by Galen it is called antyoidea because it is attached within the second cartilage in its uppermost part toward the pore of air opposite to the hyoid bone. This third cartilage is as much smaller than the second as the first is larger than the second. This cartilage in my judgment is not one alone but two united in such a way that they seem to be one single cartilage. This cartilage works in its opening like two halves of a little book, of which one half is closed toward the other, and they work in an opposite manner in its opening. This cartilage when closed in its upper and lower part makes the hole wider than in the middle. It has such a hole, or holes, as a horn has in its ends, but greater above than below. Therefore Galen said in his book *On the Assistance of the Parts* viii that for the voice to be produced it was necessary that the epiglottis first be broadened, then narrowed, and then widened once more. When this cartilage is closed, it meets the scutal cartilage; when its parts or sides are opened, they move toward the nameless cartilage.

Above these three cartilages is a fourth, a body membranous, cartilaginous, and fat, similar to the tongues of pipes (to an ivy leaf and to the human tongue). Therefore Galen called it glottis, or tongue; it is also called sublinguium. This is the most important organ of the voice. The glottis is not a member of pure cartilage, because a hard member is difficult to fold, nor is it of pure membrane, because in closing it would be doubled; but it is composed of membrane and cartilage for proper closing. In it there is fat so that it may not be dried out both by its continual motion and through breathing the dried air again and again. This member must close the epiglottis at the time of swallowing. The cymbalaris also closes the epiglottis on the hinder part while the glottis closes the anterior part so that (ordinarily [1535]) neither in vomiting nor in swallowing can anything enter the cane of the lung (except violently).

The epiglottis is made not from a single cartilage but from many, so that it can be dilated and contracted in the different acts of forming the voice. Therefore, nature gave to these cartilages, and to the throat, muscles to serve them. There are four of these;[180] they unite the first cartilage to the second, and two of them are inside to close the epiglottis and two outside.

There are four others which join the second cartilage with the third,[181] that is, with the cymbalaris. Two of these are behind. These open, drawing the cymbalaris to the rear. Two at the sides also draw the cymbalaris to the sides.

There are two other muscles near the scutal cartilage within the epiglottis which close the cymbalaris.

There are also within the epiglottis two other muscles near the root of the cymbalaris which also close the epiglottis. These twelve muscles are proper to the cartilages of the epiglottis; they are joined to none of the adjacent parts, according to Galen, *On the Usefulness of the Parts* vii.

The glottis also has one pair of muscles by means of which it closes the uppermost part of the epiglottis. These muscles are stronger than the others, according to Galen, *On the Assistance of the Parts* viii. These muscles resist the muscles of the chest and the other muscles which open the epiglottis; possibly, according to some, these muscles are the last two immediately described.

In addition to the aforesaid muscles there are eight others, of which two are proper to the cane of the lung, according to Galen, *On the Voice and Breath*. These are in the channel of the throat. Avicenna says they are at the gullet.

There is another pair of muscles that serves the throat—not primarily, however, since it also serves neighboring members. This pair continues the third cartilage with the gullet.

There are two others serving the throat; at their destruction hoarseness is caused. In this manner there will be twenty muscles serving the epiglottis and the throat.

Therefore one can understand the error of some modern physicians who believe that there are in the fauces two proper muscles that serve them, thinking that Avicenna on the muscles of the throat, i. l, for throat understood fauces as he did in ix. 3. But this I deny, since faux is not any determinate member, as I have said at greater length in my *Commentary on Mundinus*. Therefore those who intend to judge correctly do not trust in names, because the translators from Greek and Arabic into Latin, being often ignorant, take one thing for the other, and in this manner almost all sciences are spurious as a result of the variety of interpreters.

CONCERNING THE GULLET

After the throat we must investigate the gullet,[182] which holds the rear part of the throat in front of the spine. This is contiguous to the aorta artery and to the spine; from the fauces through the neck and chest it descends to the stomach, perforating the transverse septum. Some of the Latins call this gula, the servant and dispenser of the food; the Arabs call it meri, the Greeks oesophagus, as if [from two Greek words which mean] carrying things to eat.

This member descends directly and inclusively to the fourth vertebra of the chest. Then it is slanted somewhat to the right, giving place to the descending aorta in order that the motions of the aorta may not hinder that which is being swallowed. When it is not far distant from the transverse septum, it is lifted a little so as not to compress the chilis vein and in order to be better strengthened for the task of sustaining the aforesaid descending nerves. Then once more near the tenth vertebra it begins to be slanted to the left, and thus slanted it descends to the stomach.

The substance of this member is fleshy and pellicular, having in its inner panniculus long villi that serve for attraction, terminated at the skin of the mouth and lips. Wide villi in the exterior serve for expulsion to the lower and upper parts, assisting by contracting themselves. In this manner long and wide villi assist swallowing and vomiting. (According to some, the gullet also has oblique villi in an inner tunic toward the outside which retain; but I believe they expel by contracting themselves as do the oblique muscles of the abdomen.) To the gullet adhere two nerves descending from the brain, one on each side;[183] from these nerves arise the reversive nerves (called nerves of the voice. The inner panniculus of the gullet covers the tongue and all members of the mouth).[184]

The inner panniculus of the gullet is thicker at the top than at the bottom, thicker there than in the stomach, and thicker in the stomach than in the first intestine, since a resistance equally strong is not required in touching digested matter as in touching undigested matter. This inner panniculus is continued to the mouth so that the attraction of food may be continuous. (Hence it is judged that the gullet is part of the stomach continuous to it with gradation. The epiglottis and all the members of the mouth are covered by the inner membrane of the gullet, according to Galen in his book *On the Motions of Liquids*. Also the third cartilage of the epiglottis is attached to the gullet by two muscles. According to Galen in his book *On the Voice and Breath,* because of this connection the epiglottis ascends in swallowings and the gullet descends while its long villi are contracted from the fauces toward the stomach, and contrariwise the gullet ascends from the stomach toward the fauces. As soon as the matter to be swallowed has passed through the place proper to the epiglottis and the villi of the gullet are relaxed, the epiglottis suddenly descending to its former place while the oblique and broad villi of the gullet assist, along with the weight of the food to be swallowed, swallowing is performed, although some physicians may understand it otherwise. The ascent of the epiglottis, according to some, is assisted by long villi located in the inner membrane of the throat which are attached to the gullet as far as the extreme part of the mouth.) By this means the epiglottis ascends involuntarily in swallowings, attracted by the villi of the meri, or gullet, on account of their strong mutual connection, and hence it is understood that the meri is part of the stomach continuous to it with gradation.

(The epiglottis ascends, according to Galen, *On the Voice and Breath,* because in the entire interior part of the throat there is a panniculus covering it attached to the end of the mouth and lips in which there are long villi that draw the epiglottis upward [1535].)

There are some who say that the epiglottis also ascends voluntarily because it ascends when we wish it to do so, and in this way it will have a combination of voluntary and involuntary motion. Galen thinks otherwise in his book *On the Motions of Liquids,* holding that the epiglottis ascends only involuntarily. In its ascent the muscles of the glottis necessarily draw it downward. Perhaps these muscles are not moved voluntarily, for the epiglottis in its ascent is attracted by the aforesaid villi and leads the glottis with itself just as it leads the other cartilages in whose ascent the glottis is necessarily depressed. The glottis is depressed in the ascent of these other cartilages because it is fastened to its own proper muscles which are united with their lower part toward the trachea and with their upper part to the glottis. These cartilages do not ascend with the glottis, and therefore they draw it downward. In this manner also not always voluntarily in swallowings is the glottis shut by the ascension of the epiglottis. In the manner aforesaid it is brought about that no food or drink passes to the throat except at a time when the swallowing hastens before the ascent of the epiglottis is completed. Then nature with a cough expels the things that have entered the cane, if it can. For it is reported in history that to Fabius the praetor and to Anacreon the poet there occurred a suffocation, to the latter with a raisin seed and to the former with a hair swallowed in milk. The glottis is closed voluntarily by its muscles when we wish to hold back inspiration and respiration. In this manner the aforesaid muscles of the glottis close it sometimes by themselves and sometimes by accident.

The form of the gullet is oblong, dilated in the upper part in the fauces like a horn, and it is not like a cane but like an intestine whose lower orifice is continuous with the stomach where it has a notable sensation on account of prominent branches of nerves from the brain that end at the stomach. Its size is evident. In number it is one member very firmly attached to the mouth and to the epiglottis in such a way that only with difficulty is one separated from the other. It is attached also to the throat throughout, to the heart with arteries, to the liver with veins, and to the brain with the aforesaid nerves. Its complexion tends toward warm but not excessively inasmuch as it is very pannicular. Its services are to lead what is swallowed to the stomach and to bring back much that is superfluous from the stomach to the outside through the mouth. It suffers ills of all sorts.

He who diligently desires to make an investigation of the throat and gullet, let him first view their site, beginning from the lowest part and noting the gullet; then ascending let him note its connection with the throat, separating the gullet with a curved knife or some other instrument up to a point near the epiglottis, noting the aforesaid muscles, to some of which he will see that the reversive nerves are attached.

Having seen the muscles, let him separate the gullet in its highest part from the epiglottis, and let him note its cartilages, the site of the lambda bone, which with two of its larger additions embraces the scutal cartilage and with its smaller additions sustains the tongue. Let the three aforesaid cartilages of the epiglottis then be seen and the fourth cartilage, united with fat and a little skin, called glottis, by means of which the epiglottis is closed. Let him then split the tongue, noting its aforementioned parts, and let these words suffice for the anatomy of the middle body cavity of which I have given a comprehensive description, and rightly so because it is delivered to students.

III. CONCERNING THE UPPERMOST BODY CAVITY

THE UPPERMOST body cavity is called the head because there the senses take [*capiunt*] their beginning. The Greeks call it cephale. For present purposes the head is regarded as all that which is held up by the neck in which are contained the animal members, that is, the brain; an investigation of some of its parts in the anterior region has been made for the sake of a better order.

This cavity is outstanding in man on account of its contents, which have common and proper parts. Of the common parts one is in front, one behind, one at the side, one above, one below. The anterior part is called sinciput, the posterior is the occiput, the lateral parts are the temples and place of the ears, the upper is the interciput, vertex, or cacumen. The lower part is called the base of the head and of its members. Whether the head is made for the brain or the eyes we have discussed elsewhere.

Of the proper parts, some contain matter and others are contained.

The parts that contain are all the external parts, that is, first, the hairs, which are not, however, to be numbered among the parts of the head except improperly, because they are not members but are numbered as a superfluity which is sometimes useful.

Second, the skin, which is thick and somewhat fleshy so that in it the hairs may be well fixed and that it may be a shield for the parts beneath it. Under the skin is a diminished flesh or none at all except for the forehead and temples.

After the skin and the flesh comes a panniculus covering the entire bone of the head, called in Greek pericranium and in Arabic almocatim and by some zinzia mater (and the circumossalis membrane).

After the pericranium follows the bone of the head, called calva and testa by the Latins and cranium by the Greeks, or cranion, because it is hard.

The parts contained are the hard panniculus and the soft panniculus. The latter is the pia mater and secundina. The former is called the dura mater, and above the mouth in the bottom of the head below the hard panniculus common usage places the marvelous net [rete mirabile].[1]

Within the aforesaid panniculi is the marrowy substance of the brain [medullaris] with its ventricles,[2] glands,[3] worms,[4] and nerves that arise from the brain. The pia mater and the dura are by some placed among the parts that contain; the nose, the miringae [meninges, eardrums] of the ears likewise, and the eyes (and all the members of the face are placed among the parts contained in the head; they are not, however, contained in the highest cavity) are placed among the parts of the head which are contained, but not in the uppermost body cavity. They are contained, however, in the head, and so the entire face is also contained in it.

The hairs are first to be examined. They are generated by reason of the vaporous matter raised to the head from the entire body as superfluities on account of the heat of the whole body. From this matter the hairs of the head are made. They are called capilli for the sake of their purpose since they are for comeliness, as some think, and for the protection of the head from many external objects.

The skin of the head is self-evident. It lacks motion except in the forehead and temples and is therefore deprived of muscles. It also has little feeling.

By removing all the skin from the head you will see the panniculus called pericranium,[5] so made as to cover the head on all sides in order that the dura mater may be suspended in the cranium by commissures and by many other pores of the cranium. This panniculus is also there to keep the cranium from meeting the skin and flesh of the head without something in between, and so that the cranium may have feeling by means of this panniculus, and so that the veins and arteries which feed the head on the outside may adhere to it, as may those which enter and leave by commissures and other pores.[6]

After this panniculus comes the bone called cranium. Lay it bare entirely from the pericranium and examine its form. This ought to be round for greater capacity and less liability to injury. It is lightly compressed at the sides, making a prow in front and a stern behind so that its ventricles may be long, thus better to serve the operations of the intellect. Whatever form deviates from this is bad, and the more it deviates the worse it is. This bone is not one continuous unit, not hard and dense as many others are, but thin, perforated like a pipe or spongy, not very thick, and made with some commissures or junctures [sutures].

These junctures are not knotty but are toothed like a saw and scaly because they are not moved. The cranium is such that its junctures may be quite firm so that, if injury occurs in one part, the other parts may remain uninjured and so that the virtue of medicine to be applied to the head in case of brain injury may have a better effect. The cranium is also such that the vapors arising from the whole body and from the brain may easily pass out and be dissipated.[7] Therefore its highest part is thinner than any other part, nor is it very hard there, because injury does not occur at the top as it does to other parts. Yet most cunning (bilious) Mars injures everything. The cranium is such that the body might not be weighed down. It is thicker (thick) in the forehead because it is softer there. Nevertheless it has (two parts which some call tables) two tables within which there is a notable vacuity so as not to weigh down the body and so that between them the air may be implanted to take up odors. This part is softer than the others because its contents are softer.[8]

The posterior bone is harder because the posterior contents are harder.[9] The posterior bone is also harder because the eyes cannot protect it with their sight. The cranium is thicker and harder on the sides so that it may be sonorous because therein, within its substance, the organ of hearing must be located.

Part of this bone also in the occiput toward the neck is dense, thick, compact, and hard, and it is the same laterally behind the ears because the strong tendons of the neck are fastened there.[10] These have great and almost continuous movements. Behind the ears are certain sharp eminences called clavales and aculares [key and needle bones],[11] very hard, to which are attached many muscles that move the members of the mouth, the face, and the neck. If these eminences were soft, they would not resist the aforesaid movements.

Near the temples this bone is also hard because therein are the large muscles that move the jaws. Therefore all these lateral bones toward the rear are hard as rocks and are called rocky.

The lower part of this cranium is called the basilar bone; it is hard especially in the direction of the palate where the optic nerves are situated in the form of a cross. Through this bone, which is there perforated like a sieve, the humid watery superfluity of the brain descends. This place is commonly called the colatorium.

This basilar bone at its top is not level but uneven;[12] this can best be seen in cemeteries, as also other parts of the cranium and all the bones of the body may be seen. Let no man approach to view these bones who is not a lawful physician.

The number of the bones of the entire head and the names of its commissures I have set forth best in my *Commentary on Mundinus*. Thus for the sake of brevity I pass over the particular description of many things because those who write about them do not agree.

The part of this bone that first occurs is that in which the places of the eyes are situated, called forehead, which terminates at the first sawlike juncture that meets it. This juncture is called the coronalis, so called because, as it pleases some, kings are crowned in that place or perhaps because this commissure bears an almost archlike or circular form like a crown descending from the top of the head on both sides to the angles of the eye-places which are toward the ears.

Opposite this bone is another bone terminated in a sawlike juncture placed at the rearmost part of the head. This is called the lambda commissure because it resembles the Greek letter Λ.[13] This commissure has also the form of an arch or bow.

Between these junctures is another commissure,[14] also sawlike, placed at the top of the head, stretching from front to back. This is called sagittalis because it goes straight from one of the aforesaid arched junctures to the other, as an arrow stands to the bow.

At the sides of this bone above the two ossa paris in the walls of the temples are two scaly [squamosae] junctures,[15] one on each side, whose lower bones ride upon the upper bones.

The first three junctures called true penetrate directly within (the cranium); these last that penetrate obliquely are called false.

Between these lateral commissures ascending toward the sagittalis is another scaly juncture,[16] one on each side, which is rarely seen except in heads that have been macerated for some time or in those which have been thoroughly boiled. Between these junctures and the sagittalis there are two bones, one on each side, thinner than the rest of the bones of the head, which Galen calls the bregma bone and Avicenna, i. 1, calls cranium. That place where the coronal juncture is joined to the sagittal is called bregma by some and zuendech and fontanella of the head, in which the bone grows together finally in children. In that spot are placed cauteries and plasters and other local applications for catarrhs and many other illnesses. In other parts of the head there are also many other junctures concerning which I say nothing because physicians do not pay as much attention to them as to the ones which have been described.

From the foregoing the site, substance, form, and size of the head are evident. Its services and connections have been described in part and will be spoken of later. It is a single member. The number of its parts has been told as well as of the commissures of the cranium, of which three sawlike ones penetrate directly inward; the others are scaly, penetrating obliquely. Its complexion is the complexion of its component parts. It suffers all kinds of ills which, if they occur in the coverings and in the brain itself, are judged serious more or less according to the place and kind of disease.

CONCERNING THE DURA MATER

Having viewed the foregoing, so that the contents of the cranium may be more comfortably seen, divide the head from the neck at the third vertebra, then dissect the head a little above the ears round about to the inner circumference of the head in such a way that you do not injure the dura mater, always keeping the aforesaid position.

This done, lift up the entire upper bone cut away from its lower bone. Use some suitable strong elevating agency because it is on all sides most firmly attached to the dura mater as much in the commissures as in many other pores.

When the cranium is elevated, you will see the dura mater, also called meninge [membrane; here corruptly spelled *miringa*]. This is a quite thick, tendinous and strong panniculus, also porous, so that the vapors may escape from the brain. Its form is flat, extended in circular form, embracing all the medulla within itself together with the pia mater of the brain.

The dura mater extends from prow to stern doubled in its length and (penetrates) in the direction of the sagittal commissure for a depth of two inches within the substance of the brain, dividing the right part from the left. It is also doubled in the rear through its width, dividing the posterior part of the brain from the anterior part. This second doubling is not fastened together as the first doubling is, because the first is fastened together by some ligaments and veinlets in such a way that in itself there is a vacuity fit to hold something within it. In this vacuity from front to rear are many veins that ascend from the aforesaid guidez veins.[17] These veins are in that place compressed by the aforesaid doubling, and when compressed they squeeze blood to many of their branchlets which are continuous with the branches of the pia mater that nourish the brain.

Toward the occiput in this doubling is a certain vacuity called lacuna, platea, fovea, and palmentum in which part of this blood is pressed out, and almost always there is some blood in that place.[18] For this reason Herophilus called this lacuna a third vein because this vacuity is oblong like a vein, and elsewhere than in veins, arteries, heart, and in this lacuna blood is not found in the form of blood. Avicenna calls this doubling the torcular, or press.

Its size, site, connection, and complexion are evident. It is a single panniculus. Its service, beyond the services described, is to clothe the brain with the pia mater along its length, width, and depth (solely [1535]) by surrounding it and penetrating it as has been explained above. It helps also by mediating between the hard bone and the quite soft pia mater. It also assists by sustaining the veins which nourish the brain and members near it. It suffers all kinds of ills. Its severe injury is dangerous.

CONCERNING THE PIA MATER

Under this dura mater is another thin membrane with very slender arteries and veins spread like a net throughout it and immediately attached to the brain. It is called the pia mater and the secundina because it nourishes the brain as the secundina [chorion] nourishes the foetus. In my judgment it is in these very small branches of the arteries dispersed everywhere in the pia mater that the blood or vital spirit is rendered subtle and prepared so that in the substance of the brain and in its ventricles it may be made into animal spirit, as I have said in my *Commentary on Mundinus*.

This membrane is sinewy and slender. It is attached to the dura mater at its top from prow to stern by many veinlets and with some veinlets near the sides of the head.[19] It is fastened throughout to the substance of the brain, which it nourishes. According to truth (sense), the two worms located within the ventricles of the brain draw their origin from these veins and arteries by which the spirit and the blood which nourishes the inner parts of the brain are carried down within the ventricles.[20] In the walls of the ventricles also there is some portion of the pia mater that carries blood and spirit, blood to nourish the parts nearby to it, spirit for the operations of the soul, as do the worms just mentioned.

From what has been said, its substance, form, number, connections, and site are evident. Its size [quantity] is also evident; this includes not only the outside of the brain but also the inside of the ventricles and passes notably into many folds or turnings, although some say that in the rearmost ventricle because of the hardness of its substance there is no pia mater. Nevertheless, this part is nourished and therefore has veins (as the first part has), although small (smaller) ones. Its innate complexion is cold and dry. Its services are evident. It suffers ills of all sorts, which are worse than in the dura mater.

CONCERNING THE MEDULLA OF THE BRAIN

After the pia mater comes the substance of the brain, improperly called medulla, because it neither nourishes nor moistens the bones near it as the medullae of other bones do. But the bones of the head are nourished so that they may preserve their medulla.

Its substance is conspicuous, softer in front and above than behind and below. Its size exceeds that of the brain in other animals both on account of its abundance of animal spirits as well as on account of the fact that by its cold and humid complexion (in accordance with reason) it tempers these spirits, which come very hot from the heart.

Its site is evident and also its form, which corresponds above and throughout to the form of the cranium. It has many folds that are visible at first sight and also many hidden folds which are seen in its dissection.[21] Within these folds throughout, the pia mater passes annexed to the cranium itself. Its connections are apparent and will appear from the description of its nerves.

It is a single member. Nevertheless, it has two parts which are not totally separated from each other but noticeably united.

One part notably exceeds the other in size. It fills the entire cavity of the cranium from front to back. In front and in the middle from top to bottom and back it fills only the highest part of the cranium and in the direction of the larger part of the lambda bone. This part is called the anterior brain.[22]

The other part is far less in size than the first part. It is called cerebellum by Aristotle and is more solid than the first part. It fills the posterior and lower part of the head. This part has its site in the rearmost part of the head under the first part just described. In this posterior part of the brain called the cerebellum there is no cavity or ventricle, as many notice. It is well covered on all sides by the dura and pia mater, and sense demonstrates all these facts. The first part aforesaid is notably divided by the dura and pia mater into two parts down the length of the head, that is, into right and left parts so that its substance and its ventricles may be distinct and double.[23]

First, then, in each side of this duplication diligently remove the pia mater with a razor laterally along the upper and lower regions together with a notable quantity of the brain, descending for a space of three fingers more or less as you find its ventricles.

For in each side of this duplication you will find one notable vacuity called a ventricle which is stretched out lengthwise and somewhat obliquely descending laterally toward the rear.[24]

Having seen one side, look at the other. In this you will see the same thing as in the previous side. These ventricles are divided by the substance of the brain so that if injury occurs in one, it may not occur in the other. The operations of one part of these ventricles are similar to the operations of the other ventricle equal to it.

In the ventricle on both sides near the base is a pellicular red substance called a worm,[25] composed of veins and arteries, which reaches from one end to the other of each ventricle. This has motion, according to some, opening and closing the ventricles voluntarily.

Below the worms at their sides is a certain eminent part of the brain which many compare to the human buttocks in its form.[26] This part both in elongation and closing of the ventricles touches its two portions together and separates them in the shortening and dilation of the ventricles.

In these aforesaid ventricles, commonly in their anterior part, are placed fancy [*fantasia*], common sense, and imagination.

Having seen the foregoing, remove the notable part of the medulla of the brain so that one may carefully see the other vacuities of the brain, noting in the anterior base of the aforesaid two vacuities a foramen which is common to them.[27] Through this foramen the spirit and some humidities contained in them descend and pass out to a certain vacuity stretching toward the basilar bone near the place where there is a certain glandulous flesh under the crossing of the optic nerves.[28]

This vacuity is called lacuna by Mundinus, head of the rose by Avicenna, and embotum by others because it is broad above, narrow below, and surrounded on all sides by a thin panniculus as far as the basilar bone.[29] Through this embotum to the aforesaid bone therein perforated by very small holes like a sieve are evacuated for the most part the superfluous humidities of the brain.[30] These afterward in many turnings of the basilar bone located above the bone of the palate are thickened by air drawn in by the nostrils and by natural heat and at length are sent forth through the nostrils and mouth by way of the jaws in that form which is known to all. Because of different reasons it has a different substance, color, size, and form. From what has been said, the services of the brain are evident. They are of one sort according to Aristotle and of another according to Galen and his followers: look them up. It suffers ills of all kinds. Its injury is fatal, not always but most of the time.

Near this embotum toward the rear also under the ventricles mentioned before is a certain somewhat oblong vacuity whose walls are like the aforesaid buttocks. These close and open this vacuity when there is need either by the motion of the aforesaid worms which are immediately above them or by another motion caused by the spirits.

Authors commonly regard this vacuity as the middle [third] ventricle, in which they say there exists the cogitative or reasoning faculty.

In the posterior part of this middle ventricle is a little foramen which reaches to another vacuity which descends toward the place where there is the beginning of the nape of the neck.[31] This vacuity is not in the cerebellum aforesaid, as many think, nor is it everywhere surrounded by the medullar substance of the brain, but it is situated between the posterior and anterior brain, notably surrounded toward the cerebellum by the pia mater which covers it.[32]

Between this last vacuity and the middle ventricle aforesaid is a certain glandulous flesh called conarium because it is in the form of a cone or pineapple.[33] This gland in that place sustains many veins of the pia mater ascending toward the center of the brain to nourish it. This gland strains many humidities to the aforesaid middle ventricle; from the latter to the embotum, and thence they are purged away, as described above.

In this vacuity, spoken of in the last place, which is behind the middle ventricle called the rear ventricle, authors commonly place the faculty of memory. But I think otherwise.

And I say first that the faculties of cognition, reason, and memory are located in the first two cavities which are regarded as the anterior ventricle, in the right as well as the left part. The cognitive faculty of common sense is in the anterior part of it, the faculty of reason in the middle, and the memory in the posterior part.

I say the aforesaid ventricle which authors put in the place of the middle ventricle is not the place of the reason but is the path for the expurgation of many superfluities of the brain and for carrying spirits down to the third aforesaid ventricle; these spirits serve not for the faculty of memory but for that of motion and sensation, which come from the aforesaid first ventricle and serve the common sense. Hence it is understood that the nape of the neck virtually has its origin from the anterior part of the brain. It also seems both from its color and its continuation that the nape arises substantially from the anterior part of the brain, for it is continuous with the cerebellum located in the rear part. Yet it has greater direction and connection with the brain than with the cerebellum. I have spoken better and at greater length about these matters in my *Commentary on Mundinus*. (But so that the matters discussed may be better understood I have accommodated below such figures of the brain as I was able, in which some of the matters previously described can be understood, as you see.)

CONCERNING THE NERVES ARISING FROM THE BRAIN

After the aforesaid items we must see the nerves that arise from the brain. There are commonly seven pairs.[34] Of each pair, there is one nerve on each side similar to its companion. Nerve is neuron or neuris in Greek. It is a consimilar member [i.e., of the same shape and substance throughout] of white viscous substance, oblong and round in form, tenacious and hard to separate. It is an organ of sense and motion.[35] The pure nerves of sensation are softer and colder than the nerves of motion.

Gently lift the brain, beginning from the anterior part, and you will find in the direction of the upper part of the nose two white oblong substances, one on each side, adhering to the pia mater. Their heads are somewhat thick. These are called by many the mamillary carunculae;[36] they are instruments of the sense of smell. Galen does not call them nerves, for they are soft. In their direction the panniculi of the brain and the bone of the forehead are perforated like a sieve,[37] both for odors as well as for purging the superfluities of the brain when necessary, although they are for the most part purged by way of the colatorium, which is in the direction of the aforesaid embotum. There in front in the cranium is a certain notable vacuity filled for the most part with air;[38] in this air (according to some) the sense of smell is first perceived by these carunculae.

After these carunculae you will see two larger nerves which serve the eyes for vision.[39] These are seen to cross;[40] concerning this point there is still no agreement. (And these are called the optic nerves or of vision; according to some they are concave or perforated; this, however, is not visible in the dead creature.)

After these nerves there is one pair which is regarded as the second pair;[41] these nerves give motion to the eyes.[42]

After these nerves there is a third pair, which is for a little while united to the fourth pair, from which afterward it is separated.[43] It descends and is spread out through the face.[44] Within and below the basilar bone it is united with the sixth pair to be spoken of now, and together these pairs make the aforesaid nerves descending to the members of the middle and lower body cavities, and from these arise the reversive nerves.

Afterward come the nerves of the fourth pair descending to the palate for the sense of taste.[45] These are thin. Some, however, take the third pair for the fourth and contrariwise, as I have said in my *Commentary on Mundinus* where I have described the cause of such an error.

There is then the fifth pair,[46] which is sent out on each side within the basilar bone in the direction of the ears. This pair serves the sense of hearing.

After this comes the sixth pair,[47] which is mixed with the third, as has been said. After this comes the seventh pair,[48] which, because it is oblique, gives motion to the tongue and also to some muscles that serve the epiglottis. It also gives the sense of taste to the tongue itself.

The substance of these nerves is known to all; yet the posterior are harder than the anterior nerves because the posterior part of the brain is harder than the anterior part, on account of the inner senses.

Their form, size, site,[49] number, and connections are evident. In complexion they are not very dry, and therefore they do not have strong movements. They are cold by nature. Their services are evident. They suffer ills of every kind, all of them serious, on account of their connections and operations.

CONCERNING THE MARVELOUS NET ACCORDING TO COMMON OPINION, AND SOMETHING ABOUT THE NAPE OF THE NECK

Having seen the foregoing, lay aside the entire brain with that portion of the nape of the neck which is between the vertebrae which you have cut and saved with the head, noting beforehand its site, substance, number, and form. Its connection with the brain has been discussed above. Its size and other things requisite to it will be better noted from what is to be said. In its beginning near the brain is a certain vacuity continuous with that vacuity commonly regarded as the ventricle of the faculty of memory. Through this the spirits sent from the brain for sensation and motion pass to its nerves. The nape of the neck, like the brain, is covered by the dura and pia mater, as the senses demonstrate.

When you have noted these items, there remains only the dura mater, because, when the brain is removed, the pia mater is also removed on account of the firm and continuous connection of these members.

Between the dura mater and the basilar bone in the region where the optic nerves cross and where the colatorium exists, two notable arteries ascend through the basilar bone.[50] One is on the right, the other on the left, as was revealed in the chapter on the ascending aorta. From these arteries, as the authors commonly say, above the bone immediately under the dura mater are formed many very thin branches marvelously united together one upon the other in the shape of a net,[51] occupying a large place in front, behind, and at the sides.

Then from these many branches again arise two arteries similar to the first, from which are formed the aforesaid little branches. These two veins,[52] once more made great, later ascend above the cranium spread out into branches as far as the ventricles of the brain,[53] bringing to them the spirits made thin in this marvelous net.

Beside this net some say there are two glands that support it,[54] and they say the services of this net are to cause therein the subtilization of the vital spirit so that divided into the smallest branches it may be better altered and the animal spirit made. Perhaps also, by the vapors that rise from food and are condensed by the brain and fall down, its tiniest branches are more easily obstructed and cause sleep.

Yet I have never seen this net, and I believe that nature does not accomplish by many means that which she can accomplish by few means. But nature can subtilize these spirits in the smallest branches of the arteries descending (ascending) upon the dura mater which adheres to the basilar bone and ascending through the pia mater up to the center of the brain; therefore this net is not given in that place between the dura mater and the basilar bone. I have given many other reasons [for the non-existence of this net] in my *Commentary on Mundinus,* to which I refer my readers for the sake of brevity; among these reasons the experience of the senses is my chariot-driver. (And if this net is given, it is above the dura mater immediately below the medulla of the brain from whose smallest arteries therein is made a certain membrane continuous and similar to the pia mater in whose branches the vital spirit is subtilized and made into animal spirit. Thus subtilized, it passes to the ventricles by means in part of the worms of the brain mentioned before.)

CONCERNING THE NOSE

Having viewed the foregoing, I should describe the basilar bone, but because its anatomy, especially the number of its parts, is still a matter of discussion among authorities, and because this bone is better examined in cemeteries than in a common dissection, I forbear to discuss it, sending those desirous of this art [of anatomy] to my *Commentary* and to the cemeteries.

Let us then say something about the nose, which for present purposes is taken for that especially pre-eminent part which reaches out from the center of the eyebrows in an equal ridge and distinguishes and guards each eye. The lower lateral parts of this member Galen calls alaria [wings]; they are otherwise called alulae. Its upper part (by some) is called lepor and summum nasi [top of the nose]. The lower part is (also lepor and) the imum nasi [lowest part of the nose]. The middle exterior part is called column [columna], and the inner part that divides the right side from the left is called the septum porrectum [the diaphragm that reaches out] and the intersinium nasi. Some call the lower foramina of the nose the nostrils (and the path from the nostrils through the upper part of the palate to the fauces by Avicenna, fifth part of the third book, is called chaiasim) but for the present purpose the hollows located above the palate in the basilar bone are called by me the nostrils. In these the humid superfluity of the brain when strained through grows thick; of this I have said something above.

The substance of the nose is made of skin, muscles, cartilages, and bones, and of a panniculus that covers its bones. Its skin is so united to its muscles that it can be separated only with difficulty. Its anterior and inferior part is cartilaginous, but the superior part is bony. It has two muscles,[55] small but hard. One is at the right, the other at the left rather toward the lower region because both arise from the balls of the jaws. They move the wings of the nose in whatever direction a man wishes.

After the muscles there are three cartilages,[56] one in the middle and two at the sides, which are softer than the one in the middle; the latter is quite hard so that it may hold the nose, which it divides inside through the middle, straight and firm.

There are two triangular bones of the nose contiguous to the forehead perforated toward the angles of the tears with small foramina by which the humidities in the eyes can penetrate from the eyes into the nose and from the nose into the mouth.[57] Because of this penetration, the flavor of medicines placed in the eyes is tasted by the tongue.

The forehead bone in the direction of the nose is perforated like a sieve to serve for smell and so that through these foramina the superfluous humidities may pass out from the brain,[58] first crossing through the foramina which are in its panniculi near the places of the mamillary carunculae.[59]

From the foregoing the substance of the nose is seen. In number it is one member, divided however into two parts inside so that if one part is injured the other may be firm. Its form, size, site, and connections are evident. Its complexion is set down as cold and dry. Its services are for comeliness and for drawing the air back and forth to the lung. The nostrils also conduct the material sent through the colatorium to the aforesaid hollows outside them. These hollows are for present purposes called nostrils.

The nostrils suffer ills of all kinds. Their injury is easily repaired. In their extreme lower part leeches are applied for saphatim and that kind [of ill]. Their particular ill is lesion of the sense of smell, which can happen to them principally on account of obstruction caused in the foramina in the basilar bone in the direction of the aforesaid mamillary carunculae.[60]

CONCERNING THE EYELIDS

The eyelids are called palpebrae because of their palpitation [*a palpitando*]; they are also called genae. They are the little skins that cover the eyes, known to all. Their substance is made of cartilage,[61] as well as membrane, with very little and, perhaps, as some think, with no fleshy part, the muscles excepted. It is cartilaginous so that the hairs may be fixed in it, which stand straight and hard to guard the eyes better. These hairs are called cilia from concealing the eyes [*a celandis oculis*]. The substance of the eyelids is also cartilaginous so that it may better resist external objects and so that this substance may stand erect when it is opened, because, if it were pellicular, it would easily be depressed. It is covered with skin for protection and good looks.

In the upper eyelids under their skin is a panniculus arising from the pericranium which is turned inward, involving their cartilage outside and inside as far as the tunic of the cornea, with the conjunctiva in between covering the muscles of the eye. In the inferior parts in similar fashion stretches a panniculus arisen from the panniculus which covers the inferior bones of the face. (In many individuals there is some flesh with some fibers of veins immediately above the aforesaid panniculus which, when the eyelids are turned in, are evident to the senses. By these veins with the assistance of other causes there occur in the eye ungula, sebel, a kind of verrucae,[62] and some other illnesses of the eyes.)

Near this cartilage, which Galen calls tarsus, is some fat that moistens the eyelids in case of need so that they may not be dried out on account of their almost continuous motion. The upper eyelids alone are moved, the lower ones very little.

On both sides the motion of the eyelids is made by three muscles,[63] according to Avicenna. Of these, the one in the middle opens the eyelids, the two others in the angles of the eyes close the eyelids. Galen, however, *On the Usefulness of the Parts* x. 9, does not seem to reckon more than two muscles: one of these is said to be in the angle toward the ear, which he says opens the eyelids if it is moved alone; and the other muscle is in the angle of the nose, which he says closes the eyelids if it is also moved alone. And if both are equally moved, the eyelid is no more closed than it is opened. This half-closing is called curva palpebra, curved eyelid, by Hippocrates, which brings with it a bad indication in illnesses. Galen, in chapter x of the work cited above, says he never recognized the muscle described, located at the angle of the nose, because he saw a large cautery applied therein for fistulae and yet motion continued to remain in the eyelids, which would not have remained if there were a muscle there.[64]

Galen also says, *ibid.* xi. 14, that the muscular skin of the forehead and of the cheeks suffices with its motion to close and open the eyelids,[65] with, some add, the assistance of the muscles. But Aristotle, *On the Parts of Animals* ii. 13, says the eyelids are moved not voluntarily but by the instinct of nature. It seems to me, however, that they have their own proper and common motion: the common is from the motion of the forehead and cheeks, the proper from their own muscles, which have their nerves annexed to the eyelids, to the muscle that moves the forehead, and to the muscles of the temples and cheeks. Whether these nerves come from the nape of the neck or from the brain is not perceived by the sense. Avicenna says that in the upper eyelid alone there are muscles because they are nearer to their beginning, that is, the brain. These are small, and some say they are without tendons. Concerning their site there is dispute among some.

The lower eyelids, according to Avicenna, are not moved, because the motion of the upper eyelids suffices for their perfect closing and opening. The lower eyelids are smaller than the upper and more joined to the eyes so that on account of their size and separation from the eyes bleariness, tears, and other extraneous material should not accumulate in them: so Galen, *On the Usefulness of the Parts* x.

In the substance of the eyelids in each angle or canthus toward the nose there are two small foramina manifest to the senses, one in the upper eyelid, the other in the lower eyelid, through which the tears pass forth.[66] In this angle are spongy pieces of flesh which hold within themselves the humidity of the tears so that they may moisten the members neighboring to them so these may not be dried out. These humidities sometimes come from the nose and also from the brain through the veins of their panniculi.

The site, number, size, form, and connections of the eyelids are evident. Their substance has been touched upon. Their complexion is regarded as cold and dry. Their service is to guard the eyes from small, soft things. The adjacent bones guard the eyes from large, hard things. The eyelids help in causing sleep. Their hairs also assist the eyes so that dust does not get into the eyes when they are open and so that other small things do not injure them. With their darkness they strengthen the vision. They are neither so thick as to shadow the vision nor too thin, in order to keep minute objects from entering the eyes.

They suffer ills of all kinds, among others the inversion of their hairs; this is cured by cauterizing each inturned hair at its root with a golden needle. Afterward they are cured as other cauterized places are cured.

CONCERNING THE ANATOMY OF THE EYES

Having seen the eyelids, we come to the eyes, so called from hiding [*occultando*], for they hide between the eyelids. In order to see the eyes, first cut the bone of the forehead in the direction of the eyes in such a way that at least you may see each of them in the manner to be described below, noting first their nerve, which is called the optic nerve; this perforates their tunics and tends toward their center. Between the conjunctiva and the cornea (sclerotica) is a notable fatness and glandulous flesh that takes up humidities as the glandulous flesh of the root of the tongue does. The glandulous flesh causes these humidities to stream out through the nose and through the foramina mentioned before in the eyelids. By means of these, both with the fatness and the humidities the eyes are preserved from drying out.

There are also the proper muscles of the eyes, which are seven.[67] One moves the eyes upward, one downward, one to the right, one to the left. Two tending transversely move the eyes circularly. The seventh is near the optic nerve, which it sustains, elevates, and keeps from relaxing while the eyes are strengthened in continual vision. Therefore this muscle alone strengthens the eye. Some say this muscle is doubled, and some say it is tripled. All these muscles have their nerves from the second pair of nerves of the brain.

Having seen the aforesaid items, separate the muscles, the fat which was mentioned, and the glandulous flesh from its pellicles, which are really four in number. They are, nevertheless, commonly reckoned as seven because they differ somewhat in substance, site, color, form, size, and complexion. Their connections, however, do not differ. They do differ somewhat in their services.

In these pellicles, which are called the membranes and tunics of the eyes, there are three humors; some add a fourth, which they call the ethereal, or airy, humor.

Therefore beginning with the first of these tunics in front,[68] there occurs the conjunctiva, so called because it joins the eye to the head. This arises from the pericranium and from the panniculus around the bones that covers the lower bones of the face. It arises immediately from the inner pellicle of the eyelids that originates from the aforesaid panniculi; it also originates somewhat from the pericranium covering the eye sockets. This alone is truly one tunic.

This conjunctiva nevertheless does not cover the entire eye in front, but in the place where it is deficient in front of the eye in the middle is a second tunic,[69] which because it is translucent like horn is called the cornea. This tunic according to some has four slender tunics, as is discovered in its ulcers.

From this cornea toward the rear is one tunic,[70] not bright but opaque and hard. Therefore it is called sclerotica. This covers the entire eye posteriorly. It is larger than the cornea, and these two tunics are by some taken as one simply because of their connection since both arise from or are attached to the dura mater. After these, beginning from in front, there is one tunic called the uvea, coronoidea, and foraminal because it is perforated like a crown and like a grape seed when it is removed from what it hangs by or the cluster;[71] its foramen is called the pupil. Its color is varied but often black and rainbow-colored or azure.

To this toward the posterior part is attached a tunic which is almost similar in size to a grape seed and also of the same color. This is called the secundina because it and the uvea arise from the pia mater, which is called secundina;[72] or, as some think, this secundina nourishes the eye as the secundina [chorion] nourishes the foetus.

(Between the secundina and the uvea is the humor called whitish [albugineus] which in the direction of the pupil comes up to the cornea. At that point the humor is bright and more clear than elsewhere, and therefore some say that this humor is called ethereal; thus they reckon four humors. Because these two aforesaid tunics arise from the pia mater, some say they are one alone [1535].)

After these tunics come two others (also continuous),[73] one in front, the other behind; the latter is larger than the anterior one. The anterior is called aranea, the posterior retina. The aranea is thin but compact, brighter than the jewel adamant. The retina is also thin but not bright as the aranea (and the retina in part adheres to the secundina).

Between these two humors toward the rear and the sides there is a vitreous humor which resembles melted glass. It is somewhat compact and viscous. In its anterior part is located the crystalline humor,[74] like a jewel set in a ring. The vitreous humor is far larger than the crystalline, but the crystalline is harder than the vitreous and bright as a jewel.

Those two aforesaid tunics arise from the optic nerve, according to authors, and therefore they are reckoned as one. Whether they are one or two, as also the other tunics, is of little concern to physicians (to the lawful physician. From the place of continuation of the secundina with the uvea toward the front between part of the retina and the entire aranea is a humor called albugineus because it resembles the white of an egg. This humor is thin and fluid in a dead creature; in the direction of the pupil it comes as far as the cornea, and there it is bright and translucent more than elsewhere. Therefore some call this humor ethereal, and thus they place in the eyes four humors, and because the secundina and the uvea seem to arise from the pia mater some regard these two and also the cornea and sclerotica as one tunic. I have said other things about the eyes in my *Commentary*). The optic nerves are according to some notably perforated; the perforation is not, however, apparent in the dead creature. I have said other things in regard to the eyes in my *Commentary*.

From the aforesaid the substance of the eyes has been seen. Their sites are in their sockets, that is, in two large foramina located in the forehead. These do not project much outward lest they be injured by external things. Because of this they have the eyebrows projecting outward, and below they have the cheek bones. Their number, connection, form, and size are evident.

Their complexion on account of their humors is regarded as cold and humid; on account of their panniculi it is regarded as cold and dry, and in reference to their amount of spirits it is regarded as warm. Their services are known to all. They suffer all kinds of ills. Their special ill is loss, diminution, and corruption of vision.

If you cannot see all these things in one eye, look into both. At least look at the muscles in one eye and the glandulous flesh with its fat and the conjunctiva. In the other eye see the tunics and humors. A skilled hand at dissection, however, seeks more difficult things.

CONCERNING THE EARS

After the eyes come the ears [aures], so called from drawing voices [ab hauriendis vocibus] or because they are hearers of the voice [audes vocum]. Both their cartilage and their foramina are called ears. Their highest external part is called pine [pina] or pirula and lobe. The lower part is called fimbra and lobe; here there are certain veins that flow notably if they are injured. Their interior part is called scaphus.[75]

Their substance is cartilaginous, to be safe from external objects, and sonorous. They lack motion for the most part. In their lowest part some think the faculty of memory exists; therefore people who wish to remember something rub these parts. The truth is that the last hollow of the first doubled ventricle of the brain in which I place the faculty of memory stretches obliquely toward the ears, and perhaps on this account the rubbing of these parts aids the memory.

These members are covered with skin. They have some flesh, nevertheless, very firmly united with their skin. There is in them no sense except of a diminished sort. Their form is known to all. They have windings like sea shells so that the air which makes sound may flow into them without violence.

Their foramen is in a bone thicker than in any other part of the cranium. Within this bone is a certain vacuity which is closed by a certain thin solid panniculus;[76] this panniculus according to some arises from the auditory nerve, which is from the fifth pair of nerves of the brain.[77]

In the aforesaid vacuity which the aforesaid panniculus covers in front the air is placed; this air receives the forms of hearing. The air gives these forms of hearing to the auditory nerve dilated into the panniculus which is called the meninge of the ear [eardrum], and then the sense of hearing comprehends the vocal wave and every other sound that comes to it.

Adjacent to this panniculus within the aforesaid vacuity lie two little bones fit to be moved by the air therein with the nearest motion.[78] These bones in their motion strike each other; by these, according to some, all forms of sound are caused more or less according to the air moved outside.

There are some who say that the aforementioned panniculus arises from the pia mater, which passes with the auditory nerve to the aforesaid vacuity. On its origin, however, see my *Commentary*.

To see these items well requires a practiced hand, with tentacles, a curved knife, a saw, and a mallet suitable for the task, because the aforesaid items, with the nerve which comes from within as well as the meninge (corruptly called miringa) which is toward the foramen of the ear and with the aforesaid little bones, are seen with difficulty.

From the aforesaid, the inner and outer substance of the ear is seen. Its site, size, form, number, and connection are clear. Its complexion is cold and dry. Its service is known to all. It suffers ills of all kinds. Its special ill is lesion of the faculty of hearing.

CONCERNING THE UPPER JAWS

Having seen the ears, lest any part of the head remain untouched, I come to the upper jaws which are postponed after the aforesaid members for the sake of a better order. These jaws, which have only two proper bones under the nose,[79] are divided through the length of the palate by a single commissure. In these jaws are the teeth, which are similar in form, name, and number to those which are in the lower jaws.

According to some, these upper jaws are composed of twelve and more bones; this is an improper conclusion, however, because these people add the bones of the eyes, the ossa paris, the cheek bones, and other bones to the two bones mentioned before.

The substance, number, size, site, form, connection, and complexion of these jaws are clear. Their services are the same as those of the lower jaws and of the palate. They suffer all kinds of ills.

CONCERNING THE WINDINGS
ABOVE THE PALATE

From the fauces above the palate to the foramina of the nose is a broad path (called chaiasim in Arabic) through which man (with mouth closed) continuously breathes in and out. This path toward the upper part has certain little vaults, windings, or caverns placed under the colatorium below the embotum of the brain.[80] Their walls are bony, thin, and pelliculous. Hence by the foramina of the nose and through the fauces the thick excrements of the brain are carried forth to the mouth. (These vacuities are called nostrils by some.)

In order to see these well, having first seen the large foramen of the basilar bone through which the nape of the neck descends and having well investigated those vertebrae of the neck which you raised with the neck,[81] with a saw or curved knife divide the basilar bone through the middle up to the palate inclusively, and you will see all the aforesaid items very well.

IV. CONCERNING THE ANATOMY
OF THE EXTREMITIES

Having disposed of the head, in common dissection you next observe the posterior part of the neck called tenon and cervix. Its site is from the basilar bone of the head to the seventh vertebra descending from the head, inclusively.

This part has parts contained and containing. Those which contain are the skin, muscles, panniculi (membranes), and vertebrae.

The parts contained are the membranes covering the nape of the neck and the nape itself with its nerves, veins, and arteries.

Of the parts containing, some are external, others internal. Of those which are external, some are superior, others inferior, and others in the middle.

The external superior parts are called by some the fontanella of the neck; it is the place where the first and second vertebrae are joined to the neck (head). This place is called alchadam by Avicenna, fourth part of the first book, in which many cauteries are given for different dispositions of the head, and therein also are placed setons.

Its lowest part is called alchael by Avicenna, or alchel, and the middle part between these superior and inferior parts is called nocra.

From alchael to alchadam, inclusively, between each vertebra actual cauteries are applied to children in preservation from epilepsy, and it is a singular remedy.

Among the external parts that contain is also included the outer skin [epidermis], which must be stripped off so that the other external parts which contain may be seen, that is, the muscles that in this dissection are postponed because of the reason stated in the anatomy of the anterior parts of the neck. These by excoriation nevertheless can be investigated in some confused way. Cast them aside after noting their size, substance, site, complexion, and form and postponing their number, connection, and services, which cannot be integrally comprehended because the dissection of the head and of the anterior parts of the neck has been placed first. Having seen these items, observe the bones of the neck placed between the anterior parts which contain.

These bones are called vertebrae. They are seven, more thin than the rest because they must be light so as not to weigh down the body. They are such because the nothos (notiaeos), corruptly called nuca [nape], is thicker in that place, growing thinner as it descends because it sends out part of its substance to each vertebra.[1] The first vertebra (called atlas by some) united to the head in the posterior part is thicker than the other six; it also has a wider foramen. The greater part of the vertebrae down to the os sacrum has wings and eminences [projections or processes] which this first vertebra lacks so that the head can be better turned to the rear without lacerating the nerves that come forth from the nape near those processes. In this first vertebra also toward the upper region are two pits into which enter two pieces [*buccellae*] of the basilar bone near that large foramen through which the nape comes forth.[2] The vertebra also has two other pits almost similar toward the lower region into which enter two pieces of the second vertebra,[3] although there are some who say these pieces are in the first vertebra and pass into the second. The first vertebra is united to the head by strong ligaments;[4] upon this vertebra the head is turned sideways.

After the first vertebra there follows the second (called epistropheus), which differs (in that by it the neck is turned) from all the others in form. This vertebra has at its top a certain addition which Hippocrates named a tooth but which (by later physicians according to) Galen (is) called piroidea (pirinoidea) because of its sharp form.[5] This addition enters a certain pit which is in the first vertebra distinct from the foramen through which the nape comes forth, and on account of this the head is safely moved forward and backward and around or obliquely without the dislocation of the aforesaid vertebrae. This dislocation would be easy if the aforesaid addition did not resist it, because the juncture of the second vertebra with the first is more loose than any other found in the entire spine. The other junctures of the spine of the neck are looser than those below them and have their simenia bones [processes] bifurcated and small so as not to weigh down the body. (The third vertebra of the neck is called axon in Greek; the other vertebrae of the neck lack a special name.)

After the vertebrae of the neck follow twelve vertebrae to which are united the twelve ribs on both sides, and these are called the vertebrae of the back (which are called rachis in Greek).[6]

After these follow the five vertebrae called lumbar and renal; the kidneys are in that spot and two muscles called lumbi. This region Avicenna called alchatim (and in Greek it is called osphys). These vertebrae are larger than the others. The place between the highest of these vertebrae and the lowest of the vertebrae of the ribs is called glutus by Galen and acrusta by Homer. In this region the diaphragm is attached.

After these vertebrae follow three others which are not vertebrae except improperly (because they are not similar to the true vertebrae in form). These are called by Avicenna the alhovius vertebrae, and by Averroes they are called the agit bones; by Galen they are called the holy and ample bone (and according to Pollux it is also called atlas because it sustains the weight of the whole body). But this os sacrum, according to Galen, is composed of four bones to which are continued the bones of the hip [anchae], which on both sides are very firmly united with this bone. By the command of nature these bones are opened or separated from one another at birth. The bones of the anchae are also opened at such a time in the pubis where naturally at other times they are most firmly united.

After these three bones set down by Avicenna there are three others (not hard as the ones above but as if cartilaginous) called the alhosos bones and the bones of the tail (which also do not resemble true vertebrae and are not called vertebrae except improperly like the three just described). Thus commonly, in all, the true and non-true vertebrae are thirty in number. The substance of all of them is bony with some cartilage placed within their junctures. All are firmly joined by ligaments so that they may not easily be dislocated by their motion.

Their size, form, site, and connection are conspicuous. Their complexion is evident. Their service is to guard the nape and its nerves located within themselves. They are also the foundation of the entire body, but the vertebrae of the kidneys and the alhovius principally perform this function. They suffer ills of all kinds.

Cemeteries are required for investigating these bones well, together with the help, somewhat, of my *Commentary on Mundinus*. In order to see their inner substance well and at the same time their marrow, commonly called nuca, with a big curved knife divide the vertebrae through the middle from the head to the tail, preserving as well as you can the nuca and its nerves unharmed. Having made such a section, you will look carefully at their bones, cartilage, and panniculus covering their inner part and also the ligaments with which these vertebrae or sphondyli are united to one another. When you have examined these, return to the nuca, or nape.

CONCERNING THE NUCA, OR NAPE

When you have investigated the vertebrae, the parts contained within them both in the neck and elsewhere must be examined. The principal part of these is the nuca (called notiaios and myelos in Greek) with its nerves. Other parts are two hard panniculi and one soft panniculus. The hardest of these three panniculi adheres to the bones; the second, also hard, is in the place of the dura mater. The soft panniculus is in the place of the secundina, or pia mater. All of these panniculi surround the nuca itself and its nerves.

The substance of the nuca is viscous, humid with some solidity, and it is similar to the substance of the brain, although a little harder. The more it descends, the harder it grows (and, according to Pollux, it is a bit more yellow than the brain in color). It is not marrow, as some think, nor is the brain. Its form is evident to all.

The site and location of the nuca is from the lowest part of the head descending to the second highest vertebra of the kidneys inclusively, and it does not pass this place. But from this place downward all the substance of the nuca is divided into many nerves which,[7] descending to the last vertebra of the tail, are divided by themselves. The number and size of the nuca are evident. It is connected with all the members to which its nerves pass. It is also connected with the liver and with the heart by means of the aorta and with the chilis vein by certain very small veins and arteries which pass to it through the foramina of the vertebrae. These veins and arteries perforate the aforesaid hard panniculi (membranes) that surround the nuca itself, and they enter the soft panniculus (membrane) that originates from the pia mater; this panniculus adheres to the nuca and thus supports these veins and arteries so that they can nourish and vitalize the nuca.

Its complexion is commonly regarded as cold and dry; some people, however, think otherwise.

Its services are such that nerves may pass from it to the members not at so great a distance as if they came from the brain, that the nerves may be more distinct and not impede each other, and that they may be dryer and not by their injury immediately injure the brain. Furthermore, if there were no nape, the brain would be larger and would weigh down too much the lower members. It suffers ills of all kinds.

CONCERNING THE NERVES THAT ARISE FROM THE NAPE

What the nerve is I have told elsewhere, as well as its substance, form, and complexion. Descending then from the head to the end of the spine of the back there are nerves that originate from the nape. These are thirty-one pairs and one nerve without a companion.[8] Numbering them thus, the first pair of nerves goes out from the first vertebra. One nerve is at the right, the other at the left, just as they always are in all the other vertebrae. The second pair goes out from between the first and second vertebrae, and similarly the third pair is between the second and third vertebrae of the neck. Every vertebra descending (to the anus) has one pair of nerves corresponding to it either in the orifice of its companion or in the orifice proper to itself. But the last vertebra alhovius which is contiguous to the first of the three alhosos bones, or the bones of the tail, has its pair of nerves as do the vertebrae superior to itself. But between it and the first of the alhosos vertebrae is another pair of nerves, and on account of this doubled pair there are thirty-one pairs and one nerve without a companion, inasmuch as descending between the first and second vertebrae there is one pair and between the second and third vertebrae is also one pair. From the last bone which is properly called the tail [cauda] there goes forth one nerve alone. Thus there are (thirty-one pairs of nerves and one nerve without a companion), thirty vertebrae true and not true, and one nerve without a companion.

The connection of these is better known from where they originate than from where they terminate; they are connected to the greater share of members which have motion. Their site and size are evident, as is also their number. The service of the nerves is to give motion and sensation. They suffer all kinds of ills.

From the foregoing it is clear that in the human body there are thirty-eight pairs of nerves and one lone nerve, a total of seventy-seven nerves, with the exception of those two which go to the nose for the faculty of smell, which commonly are not called nerves because they are too soft. I, however, call them nerves insofar as they are organs of the sense of smell, and so there are seventy-nine.[9] Sixty-three of these come from the nape and fourteen from the brain, or sixteen if the mamillary carunculae are numbered with them. I have discussed the latter above in the anatomy of the nerves of the brain; they are afterward terminated in infinite branches and villi which cannot readily be perceived. They are as follows:

The nerves coming from the brain are seven or eight pairs.[10]

The nerves of the nape of the neck are eight pairs.

The nerves of the nape of the back or of the ribs are twelve pairs.

The nerves of the nape of the kidneys or alchatim are five pairs.

The nerves of the nape alhovius are three pairs.

The nerves of the nape alhosos with two nerves between the vertebrae alhosos and alhovius are three pairs,[11] and one nerve without a companion issues from the tail.

CONCERNING THE ANATOMY OF THE HANDS

Having seen the foregoing, I come first to the veins of the hands which are accustomed to be phlebotomized. With these we shall also see their cartilages, bones, marrow, and nails. Their muscles are postponed because they are not shown in a common dissection. The knowledge of the muscles is of great service to surgeons, according to Averroes in the first book of the *Colliget,* and therefore, because they cannot be shown at present, I place at the end

---

In this figure you can easily see the number of the vertebrae, and you can see how from the substance of the first vertebra two nerves go forth, one from each side. You can note the number of nerves at the end of the lines placed in this figure.

Note, however, reader, that this figure does not bear a true resemblance to the vertebrae except in their number, but their true form is seen in true vertebrae dried out in cemeteries [fol. 55r].

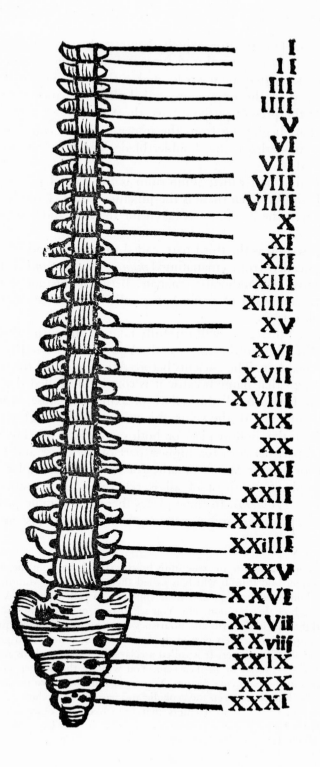

I
II
III
IIII
V
VI
VII
VIII
VIIII
X
XI
XII
XIII
XIIII
XV
XVI
XVII
XVIII
XIX
XX
XXI
XXII
XXIII
XXiIII
XXV
XXVI
XXVii
XXviij
XXIX
XXX
XXXI

of this book certain pictures which demonstrate some muscles, especially exterior ones. I place there also pictures indicating the principal bones.

First there occur two members located at the sides which from the shoulders to the end of the fingers are called the big hands by Galen. These members for the present purpose have three parts.

The first part beginning from the upper region is commonly called the adiutorium; above this is the shoulder blade, which by some is included in the large hand.

Under the first part called adiutorium is the second part called the arm [brachium], and between these is the juncture called elbow [cubitus]; commonly, however, the brachium is taken for the first and second parts aforesaid.

Under the second is the third part, called the small hand. This is properly the hand, so called from emanating [*manus ab emanando*], because from this part almost all handicrafts emanate. Between this and the second part is a juncture composed of many bones called in Arabic raseta and ascam and in Greek carpus.

Having noted these, you will carefully take off the entire skin of the large hand from the neck to the finger-ends. You will first see the basilica vein, that is, the royal vein. The ancients before Aristotle called this vein iecoraria, and it still keeps that name because it is commonly called the vena hepatis, the liver vein. It is also called ascellaris or axillaris because, as was explained above in the anatomy of the veins, this vein passes through the armpit.

The armpit is that hollow place on both sides which is below the shoulders in the lateral part between the highest part of the chest and the top of the adiutorium. Because it cannot breathe [or be aired], this place has an odor in many people, for it least of all is relieved of secretions, according to Aristotle in his *Problems*. In these places there is a notable piece of glandulous flesh which receives some excrements of the heart just as the pieces of

---

Here you see in one picture the true funis brachii stretching from the shoulder directly to the index finger and thumb which is called the salvatella by Mundinus in the little hand and by Dino and by Ugo and their followers is called sceiles. Avicenna regards this as one branch of the common vein. You see in both pictures how the basilica vein is in the inner right part of the arm and nourishes that part and how obliquely from it one branch lies toward the outer left part of the hand near the joint which goes between the little finger and the ring finger. It is called ascelaris by Galen and his followers because it is a branch of the ascelar or basilica vein. You will see this branch between the little and ring fingers in the following picture. You see also in these two pictures the common vein which is the branch between the cephalic and basilica or ascelaris vein. You see how from the common vein a branch enters that branch of the descending cephalic vein which terminates between the index finger and thumb; this by Albucasis and also by others is called the funis brachii, as was shown above [fol. 56v].

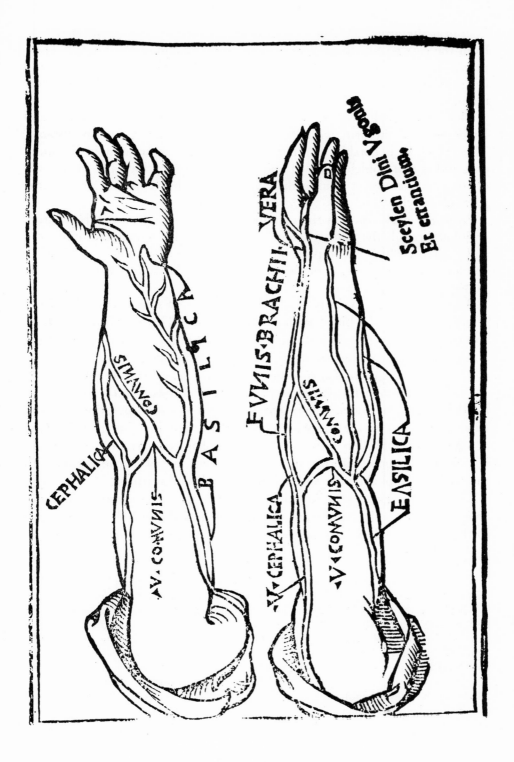

flesh near the groin and in the neck near the guidez [veins] not far distant from the ears receive the superfluities of the liver and of the brain.[12] These places are called the emulctories [milker drains] of the heart, liver, and brain. These pieces of flesh are a cushion for the large veins located near them.

This vein called ascellaris and basilica descends through the inner and lower parts of the arm with its companion artery for a certain distance. Then the vein is notably manifest alone near the elbow joint in the inner part and is there phlebotomized and brings comfort principally in illnesses of the chest because it is immediately united to the veins that nourish the parts of the chest.

From the neck through the exterior from the shoulders to this juncture or joint through the adiutorium passes a vein called spatularis, humeralis, and cephalic, which is also phlebotomized near the elbow joint.[13] This gives comfort principally in ills of the head and neck because it is immediately united to the guidez veins.

Between these is a vein passing transversely from one to the other from which it receives the blood without distinction.[14] This is called the black, common, and middle vein because it empties from the members of the head and of the chest and consequently from the entire highest part. By means of this vein evacuation is also accomplished from the lower regions.

The cephalic vein for the most part alone descends directly to the little hand between the index finger and thumb. It is called by Albucasis and Rhazes and also by me the true rope of the arm [funis brachii]. By Guy de Chauliac and by Canamusali it is called cephalic ocularis. When this vein is incised, it brings comfort in ills of the head because of its connection with the aforesaid cephalic vein and also because of its directness.

The basilica vein descending alone almost to the hand through the inner and lower part is slanted toward the exterior near the little hand and sends forth from itself branches between the little finger and the ring finger.

In these pictures is seen the place of the salvatella of Mundinus, the place of the salvatella of Rhazes, the place of the sceiles of Avicenna, the place of the salubris of Haly [Abbas], and the place of that branch of the basilica which terminates between the little and the ring fingers. Rhazes calls this vein the salvatella. It is seen how that vein which is called funis brachii by Avicenna terminates near the middle finger in the branch of the vein called sceiles by Avicenna and salubris by Haly. In this picture also is seen how the true funis brachii is a branch of the cephalic vein which terminates between the index finger and thumb. In these pictures and in the other picture are shown some small branches which are disseminated among the muscles of the arms and hands, and every vein of our body has them. They finally terminate in capillary veins. Although each vein shown in these pictures does not have them, this makes no difference [fol. 57r].

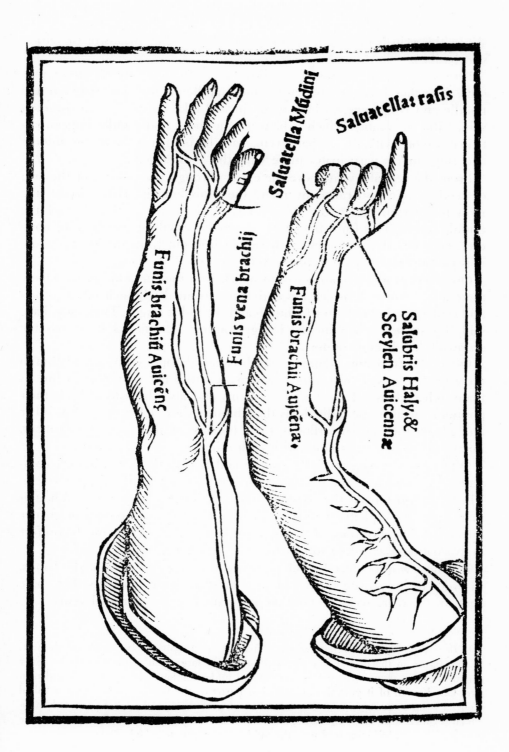

When this vein is incised, it empties from the chest by means of the afore-said basilica.

Between these two veins of the little hand there are for the most part some branches between the index and middle fingers and between the middle and ring fingers which when incised take the place of a common vein.[15] But the branch which is between the index and middle fingers participates more with the cephalic vein, and the branch between the middle and ring fingers participates more with the basilica vein.

From the cephalic vein above the elbow through the exterior of the arm descends a vein also called by many the funis brachii. This vein for the most part terminates in the aforesaid veins that exist at the sides of the middle finger. This funis brachii is not used for phlebotomy; it can, however, be cut in case of necessity. It should lead out from the head because it is continuous with the cephalic vein.

Often also from the common vein which is in the curvature of the elbow there arises a branch which descends alone from the branch of the afore-said cephalic vein between the thumb and the index finger. Thus some have said this branch when incised brings comfort in illnesses in which the aforesaid vein brings comfort.

Often also from this common vein between the index finger and thumb no vein descends. I have noted this many times not only in this but in many other veins.[16] I have seen the veins and also the arteries vary their position, and in some individuals their branches are deficient, and in other individuals they are superfluous (and because of this, in my judgment, many authors are at variance with each other).

Often also between the index finger and thumb there is a branch composed of a branch of the cephalic vein and a branch of the common vein. Then it empties from the common and from the cephalic veins, although more from the cephalic than from the common vein on account of greater directness. The directness of the veins to the members brings much comfort in evacuations, according to Galen, *On Phlebotomy*.

Let these words suffice for the present concerning the veins of the hands. In order to investigate them well you must study the pictures that come next. In these are seen the position and names of the principal veins.

In these three figures you have all the veins that are usually phlebotomized in the feet. In that figure in the middle you see how one quite large vein coming from the inner part of the coxa slants down in descending and under the ham of the knee is divided in two. One branch of it goes through the inner part of the foot or shank. This is called saphena as far as the little foot. The other branch goes through the outer part of the foot which is called scia. These branches, both inner and outer, are seen in the figures at the sides which are phlebotomized near the ankle or near the toes [fol. 59r].

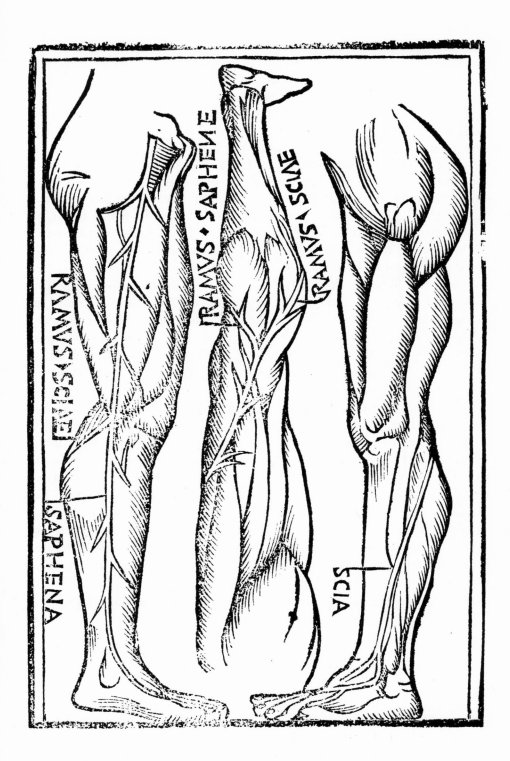

Having seen the veins at least in one hand, since that is sufficient, all its bones are to be uncovered. Then the shoulder blade is to be examined; it is made to sustain the hand and so that the adiutorium otherwise should not be continuous with the chest,[17] because then the facility of the operation of the hands one to another would be destroyed and a narrowing of action would result. The shoulder blade was separated from the ribs because of its strong motion and because thus located it better protects the members of the chest toward the posterior region. It was also placed on the sides so as not to meet the vertebrae. Toward the vertebrae it is thin and broad like a spattle: therefore it is called spatula.[18] Its part toward the adiutorium is thick. In its head there is a certain cavity called pixis in which the upper round extremity of the adiutorium revolves;[19] this is called vertebrum.

The bone of the spatula has in this place two additions. One is at the upper and posterior part; this is bound with the upper fork of the chest and is called crow's beak;[20] its service is to prevent the adiutorium from being moved from its place to the upper region. The other addition is in the inner and lower part;[21] this also keeps the adiutorium from dislocation.

This bone has upon its back a triangular substance whose basis is toward the posterior part; its eminence is toward the inner part so that the surface of the back is not raised to a sharp point and easily injured; in the extremity of this eminence is a cartilage.

Notice that this cartilage is double and softer [emending *durior* to *mollior;* see below] than any bone anywhere in the living creature. This cartilage is at the end of the broader bone of the shoulder blade, in the chest, in the epiglottis, and elsewhere in many places. There is another cartilage harder than this one which nevertheless is softer than bone. This is in the extremities of the big bones of the joints; it is called alaguahic by Avicenna. This cartilage adheres immediately to the substance of the bones, but the other cartilage in the aforesaid joints adheres to this alaguahic, and to the aforesaid softer cartilage the ligaments in the joints afterward immediately adhere, fastening the bones together. These cartilages are best seen in bones that have been thoroughly boiled.

Having seen the spatula, see the bone of the adiutorium, which is the largest of the bones of the hand. Its form is known to all. It is somewhat

---

This is a figure which shows the image of a skinned man. In it is seen the forms of the exterior muscles of the anterior part. By this picture physicians are assisted in recognizing the heads and middle parts of the muscles so that they may better prognosticate wounds, ulcers, and apostemata and know how to make incisions of wounds, ulcers, and other surgical operations without lesion of the tendons which are in the heads of the aforesaid muscles [fol. 60v].

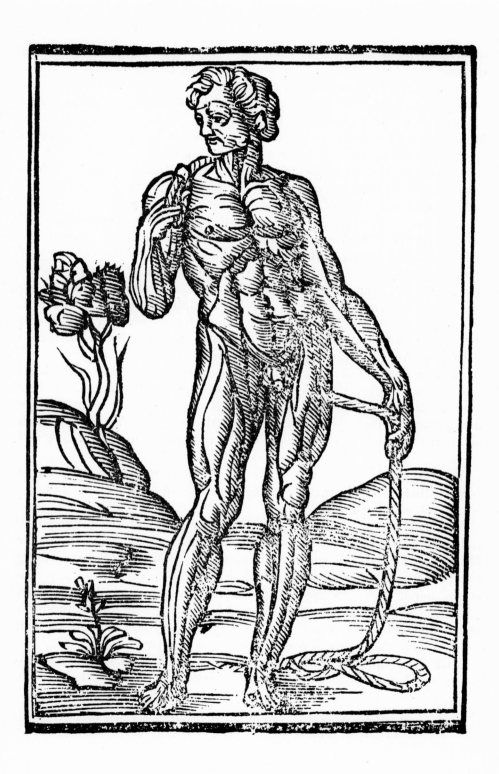

curved, and in its hollow as in many other bones there is marrow, so called because it is in the middle of the bone [medulla, *in medio ossium*].

The medulla is the nourishment of the blood, according to Aristotle, *On the Parts of Animals* ii; it is also a concocted and contained secretion, and Avicenna, first part of the first book, says the bones are nourished by it. Hence is recognized the artifice of nature which, when it does not always have veins fit for the bones, places their food in pores and hollows of the bones; and if there are also superfluities, nature places secretions in them since it does not have any other place suitable.

The lower extremity of the bone of the adiutorium has two eminences by which the bone is joined to the two fociles of the arm [from *fusillus*, "a little spindle"], making the elbow joint with strong ligaments.[22] In the hollow which is between the aforesaid eminences enters the extremity of the lower focile,[23] which is larger than the upper focile; the latter is curved to make the joint more firm on account of the almost continuous and strong motions of this joint, which because of this strengthening is rarely dislocated. If it is dislocated, it is hard to return it to its former place. The fociles of the arm are also hollow because all the bones are either hollow or porous so that they may be light and not weigh down the body.[24]

The extremities of these fociles and of all the bones and joints of the hand and foot are thicker than in the middle because in the extremities there must be large ligaments on account of the strength of the joints. In the middle they are thin so as to yield place to the bodies of the muscles which necessarily on account of their multiform movements must be many and large.

After the bones of the arm come the bones of raseta, or of the wrist [*carpi*]; these are eight because of the multitude of their motions and also because of something else.[25]

Afterward there is the little hand. Its inner part without the fingers is called the vola and palm. Its external part, according to Aristotle, *On the History of Animals* i, is without a name; its bones are four, corresponding to all the fingers other than the thumb. From these is composed the pecten of the hand,[26] the procarpus or procarpius, antecarpus, and metacarpus. There are some, however, who believe that the first bone of the thumb is in the raseta and that thus the thumb has only two bones. Some say that the first bone of the thumb is in the pecten of the hand.

After the pecten come the fingers. First is the thumb, which has two bones outside the vola. Second is the index finger next to the thumb. Beside

---

In this figure are seen the exterior lateral muscles of the human body by which physicians are rendered cautious in the prognostication of apostemata, ulcers, wounds, incisions, and in other surgical operations [fol. 61r].

this is the middle finger, longer than the others. Then comes the finger called the physician's and the ring finger. After this is the little or ear finger. These four have three joints and three bones. In my judgment the thumb also has three joints and three bones, for I do not place the first bone that serves it either in the raseta or in the pecten.

In the inner part of the fingers is a notable flesh which is a cushion for the bones so that they may not be injured in their continuous contacts with hard objects which they necessarily touch in the operations of the hands. At their sides is less flesh and less in the external part because in these parts the fingers do not meet injurious objects in their operations as they do inside the hand.

The tendons of the fingers,[27] especially the exterior ones, enter their joint above. Each finger has its tendon, of which I do not speak at present because their muscles cannot be seen; some of them are located deep in the arm, and some tendons come to the fingers from the neck, as I have said at greater length concerning the ring finger in my *Commentary on Mundinus.*

In the large hand therefore are thirty-one bones with the exception of the sesamoid bones which fill some joints. First is the shoulder blade, then the adiutorium, then two fociles of the arm, eight bones of the raseta, four of the pecten, and fifteen of the fingers.

At the end of the finger bones are nails, which are for the comeliness of the hand, the protection of the finger tips, and for picking up minute objects. The nails are generated from superfluities, as are the hairs. Therefore they grow continually even in a dead man. From the foregoing there are evident the substance of the hands, their site, number, form, connection, and size. Their complexion is the same as that of their parts. Their services cannot be described, for they are the organs of organs. They suffer all kinds of ills.

CONCERNING THE ANATOMY OF THE FEET

Having seen the hands, look also at the feet, at least one, which is enough in this dissection just as one hand was sufficient. The foot is divided into the big and little foot, as the hand was divided, according to Haly and Galen. The foot according to Haly has four parts. The first part is called the hip [ancha], the second coxa [thigh], the third the shank or shin [crus], the fourth the little foot.

First its skin must be removed everywhere from top to bottom. In its inner part under the skin descending from the groin through the coxa is a notable

---

This is a figure in which from the back are seen all the immediately subcutaneous muscles; it offers the aforementioned assistance to physicians. These figures also assist painters in delineating the members [fol. 61v].

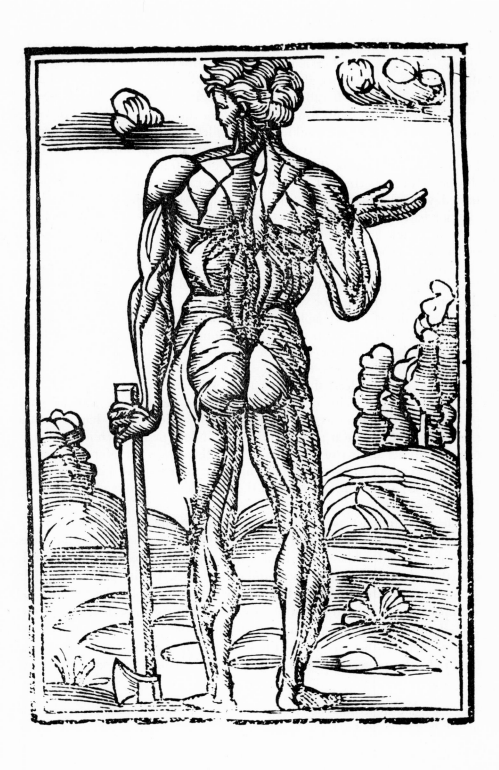

branch of the chilis vein which, when it is under the knee joint [*poplite,* "ham" or "hough"], as I said above, is divided into three parts. One descends directly through the inner part to the inner hollow or ankle [cavilla domestica] of the foot. This is called saphena; it is incised in various illnesses.

One other branch slants toward the exterior through the calf and descends to the outermost hollow or ankle. This is called sciatica (ischiadica) or scia.[28] When incised, this brings comfort in pain of the hip. Mundinus did not know the bifurcation of this branch, nor did his followers know it. Perhaps this branch brings comfort in sciatic pains because some of its branches are united with the branches of the veins that nourish the muscles and the exterior part of the hip (coxae) toward the joint of the ischium [scia].

Among these branches in the raseta of the foot are veins common to each of the aforementioned branches, and these common veins are sometimes cut, especially if one of the aforementioned two branches cannot be found, which often happens because, as was explained above, the veins do not keep the same place, number, or size.

Between the aforesaid saphena and the sciatica veins under the ham of the knee there descends to the little foot one notable branch which holds the middle between these veins; this can be cut in case of the absence of one of the aforesaid veins. In the figures that follow you will see the aforementioned veins, at least the saphena and sciatica.

Having seen the veins of the foot, you must remove the muscles completely from the bones as was done in the dissection of the hands for the same reason, noting near the groin that glandulous flesh which is the emulctorium [milker drain] of the liver.[29] Near this passes the aforesaid branch of the descending chilis vein from which the saphena and sciatica veins are derived.[30] By this flesh are imbibed the superfluous matters of the liver, as I said elsewhere.

When the muscles are removed, there remain the bones of the foot. Of these, beginning with the higher ones, the first to occur are the hipbones, one on each side. These two bones in the posterior part are very firmly united to the os sacrum or to the alhovius bones. In the pecten they join each other.[31] Both before and behind, these two bones by the will of God are opened in childbirths, and because of childbirth these bones are more curved and broader in the female than in the male. These four bones have names. In front they are called the bones of the pecten, penis, pubis, and femur. In the posterior part they are called hipbones, and above in front

---

In this figure are seen the forms, positions, and true number of all the bones of the human body with the exception of the bones of the head and back, all of whose joints can be seen only in bodies that have been boiled or dried out in cemeteries [fol. 62r].

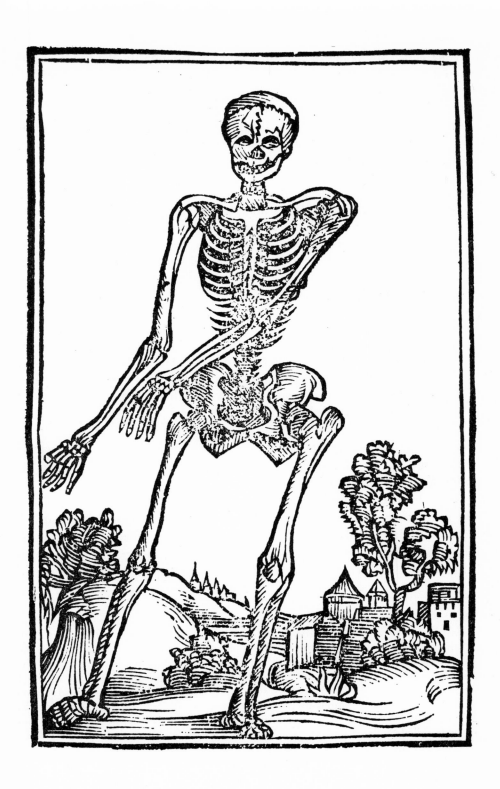

they are called the bones of the ilium and alharthapha. In the lower region where there is a hollow called pixis into which enters the head of the coxa bone,[32] round at the top and called the vertebrum, these bones are called bones of the scia and acceptabulum.[33]

Adjacent to these bones of the hip in the posterior part lie the nates, so called from being sleek and well conditioned [a nitendo], and sessus, from sitting [a sedendo]. In these parts the flesh is thicker than in other members lest the softness of the body pressing on it should press it with the bones. These parts according to some have connection with the entire body; therefore they say that cupping glasses and leeches are applied in that region in place of phlebotomy, and their senses are dull because they have few nerves. They furnish among other services rest for the body in sitting; they protect the anus from cold and serve for good looks by hiding the place of the excrement.

After this hipbone follows the bone of the coxa—long, folded inward and convex on the outside, thicker than any other bone in the body, hollow so that it may be light. There is marrow in it as in other large bones. The joint between this bone and the hipbone is called scia. This bone has two additions above and two below, but the upper additions are larger. One of these enters the aforesaid pixis of the hipbone in whose center it is very firmly united with one round, hard, tendinous ligament,[34] with other ligaments besides, so that it is not easily dislocated.

Its lower additions are joined to two fociles of the shank.[35] In the anterior part of these fociles is a flat, round bone called rotula.[36] All these bones are bound together very firmly by ligaments. This joint is called the knee; its posterior part is called the ham.

From the knee to the little foot is the leg. Its anterior part is called crea and its posterior part sura. In this part are the two aforesaid bones called focilia, arundines, colla, tibiae, and cannae. These two fociles differ in size, for the bone located in the inner part is longer and thicker than that which is located in the outer part. The smaller focile is not joined with the bone of

---

In this figure are seen the bones of the posterior part of man. Two skulls are also shown; in the one at the left is seen the coronal commissure, which is in the higher part, and the sagittal commissure in the middle. The lambda commissure is also seen in the lower part at the sides. There are seen the two commissures named by me above in the anatomy of the cranium; these are above the squamous commissures near the ears, but they are almost invisible. On the right is seen another skull in which are shown the jaws and part of the coronal commissure, the two commissures below the sagittal at one side, and one of the two bones of the ossa paris which is from the region of the eye, or from the bone called apple of the face, reaching through the width of the head toward the ears [fol. 62v].

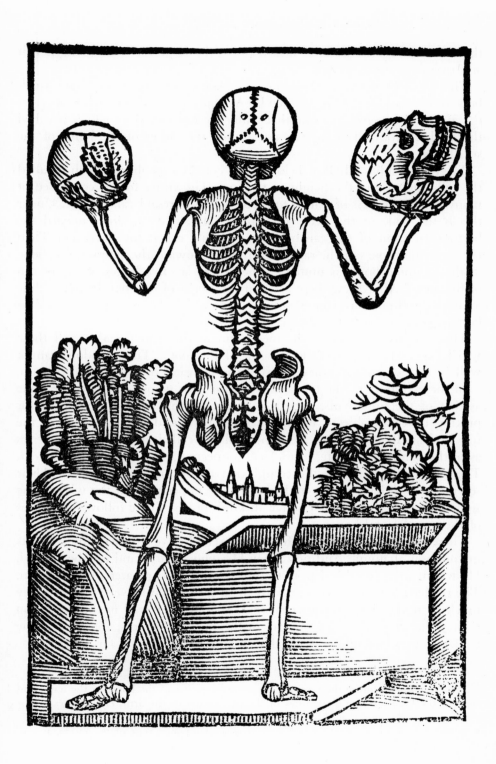

the coxa, but below the knee it adheres to the large focile to strengthen it and to hold it erect.

These two fociles toward the lower region terminate at one quite thick bone of the small foot.[37] It is called by Avicenna the cahab bone. At its sides the aforesaid two fociles make that eminence on both sides which is called the ankles. From all of these is constituted the larger of the joints of the small foot.

The foot also has a hollow below and a convex part above which is called the hill [mons] and the height of the foot. The entire foot is composed of many bones, the first of which to occur is the aforesaid cahab bone. Under this is the bone of the heel,[38] which, as one stands, declines toward the bottom. In front of the cahab bone is a bone called the navicular. Then there are four bones of the raseta with which, toward the exterior, one bone of the sesamoid bones is united.[39] Then there are five bones of the pecten of the foot.[40] After these there are fourteen bones of the toes. In the middle joint of the thumb are seen also two sesamoid bones, or sisamina, so called because they resembled a sesame seed.

The tendons that extend the toes begin in the shin [crea],[41] and those which contract the toes are in the sole of the foot.[42] These tendons cannot well be seen except in bodies wasted away in water or dried up in the sun.

In the extremity of the toe bones are also nails whose service is the same as that of the fingernails, with this exception, that they are not used for picking up small objects. From what has been said, the substance of the feet is clear. In them there are also cartilages called alaguahic and arteries as in the hands. Their site, form, size, connection, and number are evident. Their complexion is like the complexion of the organic members. Their services are to change place and to carry the upper parts at the wish of the soul as far as they can. They suffer all kinds of ills. There follow the figures of the muscles and bones.

These are the words which for the present I have given to my students in common anatomy. And now, may He who is three and one be praised, He whom most humbly I pray to direct me toward greater things, Amen. The reader who is not content with these words may have recourse to my much more detailed *Commentary on Mundinus*. Farewell in the Lord, you who gather the flowers of our art in the manner of bees, for I reject the reader of unsound mind: others I seek and honor. Again, farewell.

You have in this figure the number, form, and position of the bones of the hand and foot. In the hand are the extremities of the two fociles of the arm, eight bones of the raseta, four of the pecten, and fifteen of the fingers.

In the foot you have the heel, cahab, and navicular bones, four of the raseta, five of the pecten, and fourteen of the toes [fol. 63, misprinted as 61r].

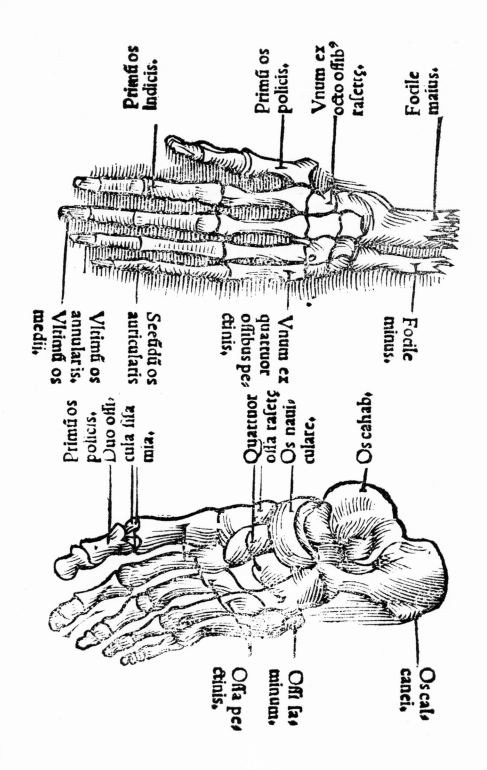

Primū os
Indicis.

Primū os
policis.

Vnum ex
octo ossib⁹
rasetis.

Focile
maius.

Focile
minus.

Vltimū os
medii.

Vltimū os
annularis.

Secūdū os
auricularis.

Vnum ex
quatuor
ossibus pe-
ctinis.

Primū os
policis.

Duo ossi-
cula sesa-
mia.

Quatuor
ossa sesa-
mia. Os nau-
culare.

Os cahab.

Primū os
policis.

Ossa pe-
ctinis.

Ossa se-
sminum.

Os cal-
canei.

DE ANATOMIA

Haec funt/ quæ in præfentiarum pro communi Anatomia Difci-
pulis noftris donauimus/De cuius fine laudetur q trinus & vnus
eft/quem humillime obfecro vt me ad maiora Dirigat : Amen.
Et qui non eft contentus De his:recurat ad noftra vberrima fupMun-
dino cõmentaria.   Valete in Dño/qui artis noftrç flores Apũ more
colligitis.Nos.n.Rabidũ lectorem reicimus/Cæteros ambimus/'ac ve-
neramur/iterum. Valete.

¶Hic finiunt Vberrime ac Breues / Ifagogæ
Anatomices: Authore eximio Artium ac.
Medicinæ Doctore Dño.M. Iacobo
Berégario Carpéfi Regij Lepidi
ac Bononiç ciue:Chirurgiam
ordinariã i almo Bononiéfi
Gymnafio Docéte.Anno.
virginei part°.M.D.xxij
fub Die.30.Decébris.

¶Impreffum Venetijs per Bernardinum De
Vitalibus Venetum.M.D.XXXV.

REGISRVM.

a b c d e f g h   Tutti fono quaderni.

Here ends the very fruitful and brief introduction to anatomy by the outstanding
author, doctor of arts and of medicine, Master Jacopo Berengario of Carpi, citizen of
Bologna and of Regius Lepidus [Lombardy], teacher in ordinary of surgery in the
bountiful University of Bologna. In the year of the Virgin Birth, December 30, 1522
[last folio].

PRINTED AT VENICE BY BERNARDINO DE VITALI

Venice, 1535

TRANSLATOR'S
NOTES

TRANSLATOR'S NOTES

THESE notes are of a textual and historical nature so as to clarify references and certain concepts used by Berengario. They are not intended to do more than supplement the Anatomical Notes to a small degree.

In contemplating Berengario's place in the history of medicine, it is necessary to note his concern with etymology, which is characteristic of the medieval period of science and derives from many sources, including the *Etymologies* of Isidore of Seville (A.D. 560?–636). The *Onomasticon* of Julius Pollux (*fl.* A.D. 158), to which reference is made in the 1523 edition but not in the 1535 edition of *Isagogae breves,* was an important source for nomenclature; it was published in 1502 (Charles Singer, *The Evolution of Anatomy* [London, 1925], p. 107). As Dr. C. W. Asling says in his notes to my translation of the *Epitome* of Vesalius (New York: Macmillan Co., 1949), "Its section on anatomical terms became the storehouse from which the Humanists replaced the current Arabic terms." This replacement may be followed in Berengario's work. Within a very few years, Vesalius dropped the etymological approach almost completely along with the previous citation of authorities, preferring to describe the parts of the body rather in terms of their shape or function, although he too in turn emphasized enumeration.

Berengario uses the then current anatomical doctrines of the three spirits, the elements, temperaments, influences, members or parts, virtues or faculties, and operations or functions. It may be pointed out, however, that he makes little specific use of the theory of the four humors, although it is implicit in his work. For handy reference to many of the terms used in this connection, see Henry Allen Skinner, *The Origin of Medical Terms* (Baltimore: Williams & Wilkins Co., 1949). Note, however, that Skinner and others who treat the subject of terminology from a popular point of view fail to give an exhaustive listing of terms, many of which must be found in older works like Dunglison's *Dictionary of Medical Science* (Philadelphia, 1874). The recent dictionaries, such as those of Gould and Dorland, often leave one unsatisfied in this matter of the older nomenclature.

The works of Hyrtl, Fonahn, and Dunglison on medical terminology have been used throughout; see the Bibliography for more complete references. References to Galen have been made on the basis of the Giuntine edition, Venice, 1625, seven volumes bound in four, done by various editors, including Vesalius.

In order not to burden the pages of the text with numerals which could be confused with those for the Anatomical Notes, I have made my references by page number, so that a given item can easily be located according to the appropriate rubric over the following notes. Frequently used abbreviations are: Galen *OUP,* for *On the Usefulness of the Parts;* Arist. *HA,* for Aristotle's *History of Animals;* and Singer *M,* for Charles Singer's translation of Mundinus' *Anatomy.*

DEDICATORY LETTER

Berengario here reveals a bit of his philosophy of science. He is not opposed to compendiums as Vesalius was, but he objects to fables substituted for anatomical writing. Vesalius follows Berengario in accusing his colleagues of ignorance: compare the dedicatory letter to Philip II in the *Epitome.* As a matter of fact, there were a number of competent anatomists in Berengario's time, even at his own university, Bologna. The reference to grains of spelt is a stock rhetorical phrase in such dedicatory letters; see also Vesalius' letter.

PAGE 37

Galen *De constitutione artis medicae* (Giuntine ed.; Venice, 1635), 3 (properties, and the simile of house vs. body), 4 (fol. 36v): "Quare nobis quoque hanc artem constituris necessarium fore arbitror non modo partes et earum compositionem verum et actiones cognoscere qua sane parte ab aedificatoribus differimus. Illi enim solas partes una cum earum compositione norunt quum illae omni actione vacuae sint. Domus etenim animal non est; verum ad nos pertinet ipsas etiam actiones investigare. . . ." From this point the discussion does not coincide with the quotation from Galen as given by Berengario. Since the wording throughout is not identical, he must have used another Latin translation of Galen.

Complexion: "Complexion in the mediaeval sense is a word which is untranslatable into modern English and is therefore left in its original form. The *complexion* is the particular manner in which the four elements or four humours are mingled together and is to be distinguished from *composition* which refers to the coarser structural nature" (Singer *M,* pp. 101–2).

". . . we must begin . . . from the whole . . .": compare "For all our knowledge doth begin from what is known" (Singer *M,* p. 59). The method Berengario follows of dividing the body for dissection into three cavities plus the extremities is that of Mundinus. The division is distinguished by animal [i.e., spiritual, from *anima,* spirit], vital, and natural members (brain, heart, liver).

". . . nine . . . [conditions or] properties": of these nine Berengario first lists substance, size, number, shape or form, location, and connection (*colligantia*). To these he adds the operation (movements), complexions, and passions (ills). Mundinus took the first six properties from the Alexandrian commentary on the "Book of Sects," which Singer (*M,* p. 101) identifies with the Greek work known under the Latin title *De sectis ad eos qui introducuntur,* K. I, 64. (The notation K. I, 64, refers to C. G. Kühn, *Medicorum Graecorum opera quae extant* [20 vols.; Leipzig, 1821–33].) This treatise also appears in the Giuntine Galen, Vol. I.

PAGE 40

Common, proper, more proper: these terms indicate the position of the parts of the body in their relation to the observer or dissector as well as their relation to one another. The common parts are those which lie at the outer edges of the lower cavity where it impinges upon the middle cavity at one end or the extremities at the other end; such parts are the abdomen above and the sumen below, with the posteriors behind. "Proper" is from the Latin *propior,* closer or nearer. The proper parts are the sword-and-shield cartilage common to both lower and middle cavities; the stomach, the umbilical area, the sumen (also reckoned among the common parts; see explanation above), the comb or pubis, the hypochondria, and the ilia. The more proper parts are those which occur first to the inspection of the dissector, such as the skin, fat, muscles, and membranes, going from the upper surface of the cadaver toward its interior. Below the more proper parts are found, of course, the proper parts, or those less near to the observer (dissector). I have considered it wiser to keep these terms instead of the English equivalents "near" and "nearer" in order to preserve the sense Berengario intended them to convey; Henry Jackson has also followed the same practice. Thus no confusion arises where Berengario uses "near" or "nearer" in contexts other than those applying to the chief organs of the body not regarded in their relationship to the dissector.

PAGE 41

Colago, itrum: Fonahn defines itrum as (1) the hypogastric region; (2) abdomen (from Greek, etron).

Acrophalus: more correctly, acromphalium, as given by Fonahn, who cites Alexander Benedictus (Benedetti), *Anatomia siue historia corporis humani,* edition of 1527, as well as Spigelius. Benedictus says: ". . . umbilicus . . . , in cuius medio acromphalium, circa quem corruguta vetula sita est." It seems possible that Berengario used some edition of Benedetti's book. Philolaus of Tarentum, frag. 13 (Diels-Kranz), is one of the first pre-Socratic thinkers to use the comparison "root" for the navel.

PAGE 50

Guidez veins: the jugular veins. Avicenna *Canon medicinae* (Latin text; Venice: Giunta, 1608), quoted by Fonahn, p. 66: "Guidez est uva quae in gutture versus collum invenitur [i.e., the uvula], et sunt duae [venae?] ex utraque gutturis parte, quae dicuntur guidezi." Berengario follows Avicenna closely. This famous Arab physician's real name was Ibn Sina of Bokhara (A.D. 980–1037). His *Canon,* one of the most popular medical textbooks of the Middle Ages and even later, was "an attempt to co-ordinate systematically all the medical doctrines of Hippocrates and Galen with the biological concepts of Aristotle" (Castiglioni). He was a sort of St. Thomas Aquinas for Arabian medicine. The *Canon* was translated by Gerard of Cremona into Latin in the twelfth century and first printed at Milan in 1473; there is also a Giuntine edition of 1523. The work is divided into five books and each book into treatises (fen), subdivided in turn into chapters and paragraphs. There is no complete translation of either the Arabic or Latin texts into a modern language; the first book is translated by O. C. Gruner, *A Treatise on the Canon of Medicine of Avicenna,* etc. (London: Luzac, 1930).

PAGE 52

Lactes: Fonahn gives four different meanings for this word: (1) pancreas; (2) thymus; (3) the small intestine ("graciliora [gracioliora *perperam*] intestina"); (4) mesentery.

PAGE 57

Melancholia mirachia: Berengario must be confusing two Arabic words by this juxtaposition—*mirach,* which means the abdominal wall, abdomen, umbilicus, or peritoneum, and *al-Mirrat as-sawda,* the black gall, melancholia. The Italian word *brisaro* appears in no dictionary, but it must mean pancreas.

PAGE 60

Chilis vein: the medieval name for the vena cava.

PAGE 61

Pontic bile: from Latin *ponticus,* pungent, astringent (now obsolete).

PAGE 64

Galen *OUP* xvi. 13, 14: "[12] . . . arteriae autem numero quidem illis pauciores. . . . [13] Inuenias igitur venas quasdam sine arteriis, sed arteriam nullam sine sua coniuge vena. [14] . . . nusquam enim vena ab arteria relinquitur sed ubi vas arteriosum videris ibi necesse est venam etiam esse, paucis tamen venis in corpora quae ad cutim pertinent sine arteriis diuisis, id quod accidit in manibus et cruribus et iisdem externis atque anterioribus. . . ."

Diabrosis: perforating ulceration of the veins. The elegiac distich is to be found in Salvatore de Renzi, *Collectio Salernitana,* V (Naples, 1859), 56, under Art. 22, "Causae haemorragiae," of the *Flos medicinae scholae Salerni;* De Renzi cites a manuscript ["ex cod. Lips. 1213") and reads *rumpit* for *scindit* and *has* for *eas:* "has aperire facit."

PAGE 66

In the year 1521: see John A. Benjamin and Dorothy M. Schullian, "Observations on Fused Kidneys with Horseshoe Configuration: The Contribution of Leonardo Botallo (1564)," *JHM,* V (1950), 315, for a discussion of this phenomenon. Berengario was the first anatomist to write on the subject. On Pallavicini see my introduction, p. 9, above, and the references in Putti, who publishes a portrait at p. 58. On quinsy, see Singer *M,* p. 107, n. 100.

PAGE 67

". . . as some think there is": Gabriele Zerbi (1468–1505), the colleague of Berengario at Bologna, is much criticized in Berengario's *Commentary* (e.g., fol. 178v). He believed there was a sieve in the kidneys. Also see Lynn Thorndike, *A History of Magic and Experimental Science* (New York: Columbia University Press, 1941), V, 508.

Galen *OUP* iv. 12: something of this sort of discussion as to drinking and voiding appears in *De naturalibus facultatibus* i. 17, at end, but not in *OUP* under the reference given.

PAGE 68

Aegitroides: there is no such term in Celsus, and Fonahn does not list it. The word must be an error for *elytroides* (tunica vaginalis, a panniculus) described by Celsus *De medicina* vii. 18. 2.

PAGE 69

"Galen, following Herophilus": the reference is *De usu partium* (*OUP* xiv. 11).

PAGE 70

Dartos: Celsus *De medicina* vii. 18. 4; scrotum: *ibid.* vii. 18. 2:

PAGE 71

"According to Aristotle": actually Aristotle argues against this Hippocratic doctrine in *De gen. animalium* 721 b 13 ff.; see also *Problemata* 878 b 5. I conclude that Berengario meant to cite Hippocrates, not Aristotle, here.

Aqualiculus: Fonahn lists two meanings—(1) abdomen; (2) the region from the umbilicus to the pubis.

PAGE 73

Field of nature: the phrase appears also in the *Anatomia Porci* (*Cophonis*), *circa* A.D. 1150; see the translation in George W. Corner, *Anatomical Texts of the Earlier Middle Ages,* etc. (Carnegie Institution, 1927), p. 53. A revised Latin text is also supplied by Dr. Corner.

PAGE 74

First digestion: the earlier anatomy postulated a series of digestions, or *coctiones,* deriving the idea from Galen.

PAGE 78

Jackson mistranslates the passage about the size of the penis in relation to the cervix: "It is as much unviolated as is the yard of him that doth copulate therewith." This nonsense is the only error I have been able to find in a close collation of his version with my own.

PAGE 82

Size of the receptacle: cf. Celsus iv. 1. 12—"Vulva autem in virginibus quidem admodum exigua est; in mulieribus vero, nisi ubi gravidae sunt, non multo maior quam ut manu comprehendatur." Compare the almost identical wording of Berengario's text: "(receptaculum) in adultis vero (nisi gravida sit) est non multo maior quam manu comprehendatur." His knowledge of Celsus, whose text was first printed in Florence in 1478, was minute.

"In its right part most often males are bound fast": this idea does not appear in

Mundinus but may be found in the *Anatomia Magistri Nicolai Physici,* a manu-script of the early thirteenth century (British Museum, Add. 24069), translated by Corner, *op. cit.,* p. 85. The idea is, of course, much earlier in its origin; see Aristotle *De gen. animalium* 763 b. 30. It goes at least as far back as the pre-Socratic philos-opher, Parmenides of Elea, frag. 17 (Diels-Kranz). For a modern discussion, see L. C. MacKinney, "Sex Determination: A Scientific Superstition," *Medicine Illus-trated,* III (1949), No. 1, 8–10.

PAGE 83

Berengario carefully updated the incident of the extracted uterus for the 1523 edition; but by 1535 the woman may have been dead, and thus he omits the 1523 description, reverting to the original. The second edition appeared about eight months after the first, as we can see by these changes in the text.

PAGE 86

Galen *OUP* vii. 21: I have supplied the chapter number, which Berengario omits. Galen's text runs: "Quod autem ad thoracem attinet, motum penitus amisisset si ex solis ossibus factus fuisset; sin vero contra ex musculis solis, inciderent pulmoni et cordi, nemine eos expellere: ut igitur simul quidem capacitas quaedam intus esset, simul autem totum instrumentum moueretur, musculi ossibus alternatim fuerunt interpositi."

"Innate complexion actuated by influence": such a phrase is doubtless based on the terminology and phraseology of contemporary writers on physiognomy, Cocles and others, for example, who speak frequently of complexion. See references to *complexio* and to physiognomy in general in Thorndike, *op. cit.,* Vols. V–VI. There was a close connection between the study of anatomy and certain pseudo-sciences such as astrology and physiognomy, much practiced in the Renaissance. Physiognomy was a popular study in antiquity; the ancient writings on the sub-ject were collected by R. Förster, *Scriptores physiognomonici* (Leipzig, 1893). Pythagoras was considered by some as its founder, but Galen, who associated physiognomy with astrology, attributed its beginnings to Hippocrates (Kühn [ed.], *Anim. mor. corp. temp.* 4. 797–98]. The doctrine of the four humors is the basis for the study of character from outward appearances which constitutes physi-ognomy. Lexicography was also influenced by this study, as appears from Julius Pollux, cited by Förster (*Scr. phys.* 2. 281–82; *Onom.* 2. 135). Artemidorus, the ancient interpreter of dreams (*Onirocriticus,* ed. R. Hercher [Leipzig, 1864]), criticized the art of the physiognomists as rivaling his own pseudo-science (Roger A. Pack, "Artemidorus and the Physiognomists," *Transactions and Proceedings of the American Philological Association,* LXXII [1941], 321–34). Galen also speaks of his work (Kühn [ed.], *Anim. mor. corp. temp.* 15. 444) and quotes (5. 463–64) Posidonius on the mixture of the elements which causes differences of character (*De Plac. Hipp. et Plat.* 5. 5). Elizabethan England as well as Renaissance Italy found physiognomy a popular study: see Carroll Camden, "The Mind's Construction in the Face," in *Renaissance Studies in Honor of Hardin Craig* (Palo Alto, Calif., 1941), pp. 208–20. The fundamental articles on the subject are by Elizabeth Evans, "The Study of Physiognomy in the Second Century A.D.," *TAPA*, LXXII (1941), 96–108; "A Stoic Aspect of Senecan Drama: Portraiture," *ibid.*, LXXXI (1950), 169–84. The Renaissance relations between anatomy and physiognomy deserve a thorough study.

PAGE 91

Galen *On the Voice and Breath* (*De voce et anhelitu*), percordium: there is no such statement that I can find in the three and a half pages of his treatise in the Giuntine edition of Galen.

PAGE 92

Galen's ape: Galen tells the story about his ape in *De locis affectis* v. 2: "De propiis cordis et pericardii affectibus: Neque enim mirum videri debet tantam humoris multitudinem cumulari aliquando in ambiente cor tunica, ut ipsum, ne attollatur, impedire possit: quippe in animalibus dissectis vidimus plerumque plurimum humoris urinae speciem referentis in eo qui ipsum inuoluit panniculo contineri. Etenim simia quaedam quum emaciari in dies videretur eam tamen necessariis nostris negotiis impediti secare in tempore non potuimus; post mortem vero reliquis corporis partibus omnibus illaesis inuentus est in ambiente cor tunica tumor praeter naturam humorem in se continens qualem pustulae (Graeci hydatidas vocant) emittere solent. Atque in gallo quoque vidimus aliquando cordis tunicam huiusmodi scirrhoso tumore affectam. . . . Inflammato autem manifeste corde gladiatores vidimus haud aliter quam qui cardiaca syncopa pereunt, obisse."

PAGE 93

Sun of the microcosm: see a discussion of the Renaissance juxtaposition of macrocosm and microcosm, man and universe, in Charles Singer's article on Hildegard of Bingen in his *Studies in the History and Method of Science* (Oxford, 1917), Vol. I, and in his "The Dark Ages and the Dawn," in F. S. Marvin (ed.), *Science and Civilization* (Oxford, 1923).

Aristomenes the Messenian: the story is told by Pliny, *Natural History* xi. 184–85, and repeated by Dio Chrysostom, *Oration* 35. 2. Galen discusses the relation of character and the four humors (Kühn [ed.], *In Hipp. de Nat. 1 Comm.* 15. 97). Förster collects the passages which show Galen's use of physiognomical material (*Scr. phys.* 2. 241–49, 283–99). Pliny (*N.H.* xi. 14) chides Aristotle for believing in a form of physiognomy. "Further, all blooded animals have a heart and a diaphragm or midriff" (D'Arcy W. Thompson [trans.], Arist. *HA* ii. 15).

PAGE 94

Pyramid: this idea of the relation between fire and a pyramid appears also in Mundinus. "In general, the description of the heart by Mundinus is borrowed from Avicenna, who in turn took it from Aristotle. The absurd idea that 'what is hot must be pyramidal' is a mediaeval commonplace of Peripatetic origin. It does not occur in the chapter on the heart in the *Canon* of Avicenna" (Singer *M*, p. 105, n. 82).

PAGE 95

Inuli: I cannot find this word in the Latin dictionaries or in Fonahn. Stephanus' *Greek Dictionary* gives *inoeides,* Fibrae similis, Nervosus. Fonahn lists *inae* (Benedictus ii. 10: "*ines* capillamenta sive filamenta sunt nervorum et fibrae stamineneum [*sic*] . . . filamentum stamineum (stomachi)."

Lacertus: long, spindle-shaped muscle, so called from its resemblance to a lizard (*lacerta*). "Sed nihil intelligunt qui cor musculum esse dicunt . . ." (Galen *De anatom. administr.* vii. 8).

PAGE 97

Flexor, girgilus: arcus aortae (Hyrtl).

PAGE 98

Galen *OUP* xvi. 10 (Berengario gives the wrong chapter, 11): "Divisio autem ipsarum (ut supra monui) fuit inaequalis quod in animali plures sub corde quam supra cor sint partes, atque quae pars arteriae deorsum fertur tanto est maior ea quae ad iugulum ascendit quanto partes inferiores numero superiores excedunt. Haec certe non sunt parua aequitatis et artificii opera."

". . . partridges have two hearts": Aristotle *De gen. animalium* 773 a 10, discusses animals with two hearts as two embryos confused, without mentioning the partridge. Pliny *N.H.* xi. 70: ". . . in Paphlagonia bina perdicibus corda."

PAGE 100

Rete mirabile: Fonahn gives a list of the various interpretations of this item. Berengario understood it as branches of arteries around the hypophysis and infundibulum cerebri, but in his extended discussion of it he denies he was ever able to find it.

PAGE 102

Aristotle *On the Parts of Animals* iii. 3: there is no passage which reads exactly to this effect in the book referred to by Berengario. Galen *OUP* viii. 1 (the 1523 edition has the wrong reference): "Sed colli quidem generationem non difficile, quis inveniat; videtur enim semper una cum pulmone interire, quam ob rem pisces omnes, quod pulmonem non habeant, colo carent, quibus animalibus inest pulmo his omnino etiam collum adest."

PAGE 103

Celsus iv. 1, 2: "circa guttur venae grandes quae sphagitides nominantur, itemque arteriae, quas carotidas vocant." Since Celsus does not use the word "granges," I am tempted to believe that it is simply a corruption of the adjective *grandes* in this passage, or at least a misreading by Berengario. The other words he uses for the jugular veins are also corruptions of the Greek word. Since "guidez" is the Arabic word, we cannot suppose that "granges" comes from that language.

PAGE 104

Parasphagis: the term is found in Pollux 2. 133. Galen *OUP* xii. 8: "... eum prius exercitatum esse oportet qui volet quae hic dicuntur exacte assequi. [Above] ... nulla enim oratio queat exprimere exacte adeo atque informare ea quae apparent ut visus ac tactus."

PAGE 106

Galen *OUP* xiv. 8: "Cum enim partes utraque ad unum opus obeundum comparasset, ipsas coniunxit per vasa quae, dum de thorace ageremus, ad mammas venire memoravimus, venas et arterias ad hypochondria ac totum hypogastrium deducendo, post autem iis quae a partibus infernis sursum feruntur, coniugendo, a quibus venae ad matricem ac scrotum perveniunt. Quae causa est cur eodem tempore menstrua belle procedere nequeant et femina lactare. . . ."

PAGE 107

Hippocrates *On Air and Water* (*On Airs, Waters, Places* 22): referring to varicose veins among the Scythians, Hippocrates says: "They treat themselves by their own remedy which is to cut the vein which runs behind each ear ... vessels behind the ears which, if cut, cause impotence and it seems to me that these are the vessels they divide" (John Chadwick and W. N. Mann [trans.], *The Medical Works of Hippocrates* [Oxford: Blackwell, 1950]).

PAGE 108

Palmentum: confluens sinuum (torcular Herophili); Fonahn, p. 112.

PAGE 110

Further information on the various coagulants mentioned may be found in the dictionaries, especially Dunglison's, which keeps many of the old words. Pissasphalt is mineral pitch, a thicker kind of rock oil, synonymous with glutinous bitumen, Malta bitumen, and mineral tar. The dried human flesh seems to have been a kind of secret home remedy used by Berengario's father also. See Roth, *Andreas Vesalius,* p. 39, and Berengario, *De fractura cranei* (1535 ed.), p. 92: "Hoc ceratum debet esse de parte capitis hominis et illa mumia de qua loquor est caro humana sicca." Berengario used this homeopathic material as a headsalve for wounds. Colcothar has many other names, but it is a red oxide of iron obtained by calcining sulphate of iron to redness, with or without the contact of air (Dunglison, *s.v.* "Colcothar"). Among its other names are c. vitrioli, Henricus rubens, chalcitis, rouge, tritoxydum ferri, sulphas ferri calcinatum, and crocus martis vitriolatus. Armenian bole is a pale, reddish clay used in tooth powders and sometimes for aphthae (Dorland). It is found in other countries than Armenia and is also called argilla ferruginea rubra or rouge; it was once esteemed as a tonic and astringent, applied as a styptic. It consists of argil mixed with lime and iron and is now scarcely if ever used (Dunglison). Dragon's blood is astringent resin from ratan palms and certain tropical trees. Galen *On the Voice and Breath:* "Et duo nerui qui oriuntur a cerebro diuiduntur in quatuor ramos unusquisque et currunt super radices costarum ex superiori ad inferius, et unus eorum intrat cor et pulmonem, alius stomachum. . . ."

PAGE 111

Bacham: ansa nervi laryngei recurrentis (Hyrtl). Galen *On the Assistance of the Parts* viii. 2: this is an abbreviated Latin translation of an Arabic version of the first nine books of the *De usu partium corporis humani* which is in seventeen books (Singer *M*, p. 100, n. 4).

Galen *OUP* vii. 14: ". . . quod ego primus omnium sacra haec quae nunc in manibus sunt inveni, quandoquidem nemo anatomicorum neque horum nervorum aliquem neque eorum quicquam quae in laryngis constructione superius dicta fuerunt perceperat. . . . [Above] Si igitur cor neruorum esset principium (ut nonnulli arbitrantur omnium quae ad anatomen pertinent prorsus ignari) facile utique praedictos sex musculos neruis secundum rectitudinem immissis mouisset eandemque nobis afferet in aliis musculis dubitationem qui capita superne habentes fine suo in inferiore in partes a sese mouendas inseruntur. Nunc vero cum satis constet neruum omnem manare vel a cerebro vel a spinali medulla. . . ."

PAGE 112

Galen *On the Inner Parts* iv. 16: this is actually the *De locis affectis,* translated from the Greek in the thirteenth century; some manuscripts of it are found under the name *De interioribus membris*. The reference is chapter 6, not 16: "His itaque quinque inter se consequentia quadam conuenientibus, expiratione, exufflatione citra strepitum, strepenti exufflatione, voce, loquela, si earum prima laedatur, reliquas omnes laedi necesse est."

Facies: Berengario, or the source he uses, plays on the words for "face" and "making," *facies* and *faciens*. Vultuosi: Jackson translated this "brazen-faced." Berengario uses the word in a sense directly opposite to that given in *Harper's Latin Dictionary,* "of expressive countenance." Perhaps "affected," the last meaning given in *Harper's,* would be the best general translation of the word, since it connotes neither mobility nor immobility of features but a sort of set expression. This discussion of the face emphasizes again the importance of physiognomy in the study of Renaissance anatomy, useful as it was for diagnosis.

PAGE 113

Varro: Lactantius (Lucius Caelius Firmianus Lactantius, who lived at the beginning of the fourth century A.D.) quotes Varro in his *De opificio Dei* viii, a work written between A.D. 305 and 311: "a quo foratu frontem nominatam Varro existimavit" (Migne, *Patrologia Latina,* Vol. VII, col. 35).

PAGE 115

Lactantius *De opificio Dei,* col. 44: "Labra ipsa, quae quasi antea cohaerebant, quam decenter intercidit; quorum superius sub ipsa medietate narium lacuna quadam levi, quasi valle signavit, inferius honestatis gratia foras molliter explicavit."

Philtron: the term is found in Pollux *Onomasticon* 2. 90 and in Rufus Medicus *Onom.* (Peri Onomasias) 39.

PAGE 116

Thick lips: another reference to physiognomy.

Galen *OUP* xi. 16 (misprinted 14 in the Giuntine edition): "Quandoquidem per quatuor musculos motus octo effecit, quatuor quidem obliquos in utroque labio duos propter eos autem alios rectos quatuor. . . ."

PAGE 118

Galen *OUP* iv. 8: "Ob id ipsum autem etiam tunica haec communis ori, stomacho, ac ventriculo . . . fuisse contumacissimum."

Teeth "harder than bone": Celsus viii. 1. 9, "Duriores osse dentes sunt." See also Arist. *HA* ii, 3. 501 b.

Arist. *HA* ii. 3. 501 b: "Males have more teeth than females in the case of human beings. . . ."

PAGE 120

Arist. *HA* i. 11. 492 b: "Parts of the mouth are the roof or palate. . . ."

PAGE 121

Cola, alcola: aphthae or thrush, sore mouth (Dunglison).

Uvula: Arist. *HA* i. 11. 493 a.

Ligando: Lactantius, *De opificio Dei* x Migne, *PL,* Vol. VII, col. 44), gives this derivation from Varro.

PAGE 122

Galen discusses the dilation of the penis and the tongue in *De motibus manifestis et obscuris* in the chapters entitled "De motu virgae" and "De motu linguae." There is no such book as *De motibus liquidis;* see Singer *M,* p. 107, n. 102. Galen's work is contained in the Giuntine edition, Vol. VII.

PAGE 124

Aristotle *De partibus animalium* ii. 17. 660 a; Galen *De voce et anhelitu* (Tractatus Secundus): "Voci et orationi posita sunt tria membra, lingua et epiglottis et trachea arteria."

PAGE 125

Pliny *N.H.* xi. 68: "Man and swine alone suffer from swollen throat, usually because of bad drinking water." For "granges" see note for p. 103.

Antiades, paristhmia: Celsus vii. 12; he also speaks of the tonsils (2) but does not call them glands.

PAGE 127

Galen *OUP* xi. 3: "Si igitur, quemadmodum Hippocrates dixit, quae propinqua, quae communia, et quae prima sunt, maxime laeduntur, nihil autem propinquius cerebro quam temporales musculi neque quiuis alius musculus per plures neruos cerebro communicat, consentaneum est principium exaudire quam celerrime ac sentire ipsorum affectus."

Alhiliricti: an error for alhibriati, processus styloideus, the styloid process (Fonahn).

PAGE 130

Galen *De voce et anhelitu* (Tractatus Secundus): "Humiditas autem epiglottidis facit voci grauitatem: siccitas vero acuitatem. . . . Et ideo magis accidit raucedo senibus, propter multas superfluitates quae generantur in eis."

PAGE 131

Cymbalaris: the arytenoid cartilage; see Singer *M,* p. 108, n. 105.

PAGE 132

Galen *OUP* vii. 11: "Mouetur autem a musculis secundum propriam quidem suam compositionem duodecim; quatenus vero communionem habet cum partibus vicinis, ab aliis octo."

PAGE 133

". . . translators from Greek and Arabic": the first complete Latin translation of the works of Galen was that by Diomedes Bonardo, a physician of Brescia, published in 1490 at Venice by Filippo Pinzio da Caneto. The first Giunta edition is that of 1541, at Venice.

PAGE 134

Galen *De motibus manifestis et obscuris* ("De motu gutturis in deglutiendo"): "Et illud est quam una tunicarum oesophagi, scilicet, interior in sua natura neruosa, cuncta quae sunt in ore et nodo gutturis inuoluit."

Galen *De voce et anhelitu* (Tractatus Secundus): "Et sunt ibi duo musculi continui continentes radicem tertiae chartilaginis." (Tractatus Tertius): ". . . sunt et alii duo musculi extra qui continuant tertiam chartilaginem cum oesophago."

Galen *De motibus manifestis et obscuris* (Tractatus Quartus): "Quidam putauerunt quod actio anhelitus fit naturalis, cum fiat in somno et vigilia aequaliter et sine voluntate. Alii dicunt ipsum esse voluntarium quoniam quando volumus anhelamus et quando volumus retinemus et hoc est verum secundum nos, ut patet ex nostra anatomia. Alii dicunt quod est medius inter voluntatem et naturam." Pliny *N.H.* vii. 7, tells the stories about Fabius and Anacreon. See also Val. Max. 9. 8 (p. 135).

PAGE 137

Cranion: *cranaos* means "hard" in Greek.

PAGE 138

". . . cunning Mars": see the Introduction for Berengario's attendance upon Lorenzo de' Medici, wounded in March, 1517, while attacking the forces of Francesco della Rovere. His experience with wounds of war must have been extensive.

PAGE 140

Zuendech: locus fonticuli frontalis (Hyrtl) and sutura sagittalis.

PAGE 142

Arist. *HA* i. 16. 494 b 32: "The brain in all cases is bilateral. Behind this, right at the back, comes what is termed the 'cerebellum,' differing in form from the brain as we may both feel and see."

PAGE 143

Embotum: Berengario believed he had seen more in the brain than other anatomists had seen. *Commentary,* fol. 429 b: "In dictis nostris tamen, auxilium imploramus a Domino quia speramus de cerebro aliqua in lucem ponere posteris nostris non inutilia. . . ." Fol. 436 a: "Ista tamen non possum ad plenum scribi, sed indigent praesentiali ostensione, tamen solers medicus per scripturam potest si non totum quod scribitur intelligere saltem intelligit aliquam partem et forte partem maiorem." Here as elsewhere his tone is one of excessive modesty, an exceedingly rare quality in men of learning in his time.

PAGE 148

Miss Nabia Abbott, of the Oriental Institute of the University of Chicago, writes that "perhaps *saphatim* minus the *-im* can be derived from *saffa* or *shaffa;* it may then refer to medical treatment of some minor misfunction of mouth or nose."

PAGE 149

Ungula means hoof or claw; sebel is an Arabic word; verrucae refers to infectious papilloma. None of these diseases is listed in Galen's long account of the diseases of the eye in *Ascripta introductio seu medicus* (Giuntine ed.), Vol. I, chap. 15, fols. 58–59.

Galen *OUP* x. 9: "Ante autem docuimus tarsum hunc esse. . . . Quando igitur musculus prior dictus agit partem palpebrae sibi continuam, quae est ad nasum, deorsum trahit. . . . Quod si uterque eodem tempore tendant iuxta palpebram . . . quare accidet ut oculus non magis fit apertus quam clausus: eaque palpebrae figura est quam Hippocrates κάμπυλον, id est, curvam ac reflexam appellauit, quam in morbis magni mali signum numerat." *Ibid.,* chap. 10: "Anatomicorum quidem certe praestantissimi naturae in palpebris artificium inuenisse ac pulchre exposuisse videntur, ut iam diximus; ego vero ipsis omnino iam assentirer si mihi persuadere possem vidisse me perspicue eum musculum qui est ad maiorem angulum. Nunc autem neque illum aperte vidi unquam et in αἰγιλώπων curatione chirurgica non modo abscinditur plerumque, verum etiam locus in ille totus sic aduritur ut nonnumquam squamae a subiectis ossibus abscendant, cum interea palpebra ad motum nihil impediatur: ob eam causam videtur mihi indigere animaduersione." *Ibid.* xi. 14: "Ad utraque igitur utilitates natura cuti omni ipsis circumfusae tum ei quae supra in fronte est tum ei quae infra est ad malas, motum voluntarium adhibuit ut alternatim tum extensa tum rursus in seipsam replicata aperire oculos ac claudere queat." Aristotle *Parts of Animals* ii. 13. 657 b: "It is as a still further safeguard that all these animals blink, and man most of all; this action (which is not performed from deliberate intention but from a natural instinct) serving to keep objects from falling into the eyes. . . ."

PAGE 150

Galen *OUP* x. 10: "At positio huius discriminis est causa; si enim palpebra inferior longior quam nunc est extitisset non fuisset similiter constans, sed in se ipsam defluens corrugaretur laxaque fieret ab oculoque discederet et quod his adhuc est maius colligeretur in ea lippitudo ac lachryma et eiusdem generis omnia quae in excernendo difficultatem haberent."

PAGE 153

On the naming of the ears see again Lactantius *De opificio Dei* vii (Migne, *PL,* Vol. VII, col. 36): "Eas igitur aures (quibus est inditum nomen a vocibus *haurien-dis,* unde Virgilius. . . . Vocemque his auribus hausi" (*Aen.* 4. 359).

Scaphus: "inner portion of the pinna" (Hyrtl). Pliny *N.H.* xi. 103: "The memory is seated in the lobe of the ear, the place that we touch in calling a person to witness. . . ."

PAGE 154

Chaiasim: the ethmoidal cells. Avicenna (A.B.): "chaisun vel chisum significat foramen seu concavitatem ossis in naso existentis et est numeri singularis: chaiasin vero numeri pluralis" (Fonahn).

PAGE 156

Alchadam: the hollow of the neck (Fonahn). Alchael (alchaela), according to Avicenna: ". . . sunt duae eminentiae posterioris capitis et vicinae duabus venis situatae in latere colli ad caput ascendentibus." Nocra: hollow of the neck (Fonahn).

Actual cauteries: see Dunglison, *s.v.* "Cauterium," for the use of the term.

PAGE 157

Simenia (Avicenna): processus spinosi (vertebrarum); see sensasen, seuasen (Fonahn).

Glutus: the loin. Acrusta: the lower part of the back, regio lumbalis, the lumbar region (Fonahn). The latter word is not used by Homer and is not found in Liddell-Scott-Jones, *A Greek-English Lexicon* (Oxford University Press, 1940).

PAGE 160

Averroes (A.D. 1126–98), Arab physician and philosopher; his *Colliget* is an encyclopedic medical work.

PAGES 162–64

Aristotle *Problems* ii. 6. 867 a: "It is those regions of the body and the substances of which they are composed through which the air does not circulate that are malodorous." *Ibid.* xiii, 8. 908 b: "Why has the armpit a more unpleasant odor than any other part of the body? Is it because it is least exposed to the air?"

Albucasis: an Arab physician and surgeon who died *circa* A.D. 1013. Rhazes: another famous Arab medical man, lived A.D. 865–925. Guy de Chauliac (1300–68) was the most famous French surgeon of his day, an expert on skull fractures, whom Berengario quotes frequently in *De fractura cranei*. He owned a copy of Chauliac's *Chirurgia* (called in Italy "un Guidone") and bequeathed it to his nephew Gaspare. Canamusali de Baldac wrote a treatise on the illnesses of the eyes which was printed in the 1499 and 1513 editions of the *Collectio Chirurgica Veneta* (Venice: Ottaviano Scoto, 1497); Berengario also owned a copy of this book.

Haly Abbas (A.D. 930–94): another famous Arab physician; he wrote *The Perfect Book of the Art of Medicine,* translated into Latin by Constantinus Africanus of Montecassino around 1180 with the title *Pantegni.* Another translation was published at Venice in 1492.

PAGE 166

Galen *De venae sectione* (*On Phlebotomy*): I have found no exact statement of this sort in the two treatises on venesection by Galen. In *De curandi ratione per sanguis missionem,* chap. 16, however, I find this: "Porro tam perspicuum saepe celereque remedium quae e directo affectis partibus venae secantur afferunt, ut et qui patiuntur et familiares ipsorum saepenumero obstupescant." Berengario may have had this sentence in mind when he wrote the reference to Galen.

In the description of the illustration at fol. 56v, Dino is Dino del Garbo, who died in 1327; Putti, p. 114, says that among the books Berengario gave to his nephew Gaspare was a copy of Dino's commentary on the First Fen, Fourth Book, of Avicenna. Ugo of Lucca was a physician who died in 1252.

PAGE 168

Alaguahic: Fonahn lists only the ear cartilages, or the auricles under this; he does not seem to know this particular cartilage under that name.

PAGE 170

Aristotle *Parts of Animals* ii. 651 b: "The marrow also is of the nature of blood. . . ." *Ibid.* 652 a: "The substance contained within the bones is the nutriment out of which these are formed. Now the universal nutriment, as already stated, is blood. . . . It (the marrow) is evidently the surplus of the sanguineous nutriment apportioned to the bones. . . ."

Arist. *HA* i. 15. 494 a: "The outside or back of the hand is sinewy and has no specific designation."

PAGE 176

Alharthapha: os ilium (Fonahn); he spells the word alhartafa, alhartapha.

PAGE 178

Cahab, cahabin: malleoli, caab (see alcahab, chahab, caib)—(1) talus (or astragalus); (2) malleolus (Fonahn).

PAGE 180

Colophons of the editions of *Isagogae breves:* the 1535 edition reproduces the colophon of the first edition, printed on December 30, 1522; the 1523 edition gives in its colophon the date July 15, 1523.

ANATOMICAL
NOTES

ANATOMICAL NOTES

THESE notes attempt to identify all the parts of the body described by Berengario and are expressed in modern terminology according to the standard dictionaries and to the *Nomina anatomica* as revised by the International Anatomical Nomenclature Committee (Baltimore: Williams & Wilkins Co., 1956). The latest anatomical atlases have also been used.

Each identification has been made as concise as possible in order to guide the scientifically trained reader through Berengario's text, although part of the reader's pleasure will consist in the identifications he will make as he proceeds and amplifies the sometimes rather vague descriptions by Berengario. The latter's use of Latin as far as individual terms are concerned is much less extensive than that of the modern student or teacher of anatomy; this is true also for other Renaissance anatomists. It is the modern age that has utilized Latin most fully in forming the exact multiple-word terms for anatomical nomenclature, building of course upon the work of the earlier anatomists.

Where the identification is merely conjectural or uncertain, that fact is indicated by a question mark or a qualification. The trained anatomist will naturally discover some deviations from modern method in the work of Berengario, but the points where modern knowledge agrees with him are vastly more numerous.

Common abbreviations used in the following notes are: a., artery; m., muscle; n., nerve; v., vein.

PAUL G. ROOFE

I. CONCERNING THE ANATOMY OF THE LOWER CAVITY

1. Splanchnic nerves?

2. Mesenteric and visceral arteries.

3. m. iliopsoas, probably.

4. vv. mesenterica, superior et inferior; vv. intestinales; vv. colicae dextra et sinistra.

5. a. renalis; v. renalis.

6. Cisterna chyli, which gives origin to the thoracic duct.

7. Umbilical veins and arteries; these are actually not adult structure. The meaning here is uncertain.

8. Seminal vessels, arteries, and veins. The didymi are the testes.

9. (2) m. obliquus externus abdominis; (2) m. obliquus internus; (2) m. rectus abdominis; (2) m. transversus abdominis.

10. Vagina recti abdominis.

11. Peritoneum.

12. Renal vertebrae, eleventh thoracic to the upper border of the third lumbar vertebrae.

13. v. epigastrica superficialis.

14. a. epigastrica superficialis. The acrophalus is the extremity of the umbilical cord; see the translator's note on this word, p. 41.

15. The "vein" becomes a ligament, and the "arteries" are the v. mesenterica inferior.

16. a. iliacae communis et externa, a. epigastrica inferior.

17. m. obliquus externus et internus.

18. Musculus rectus abdominis.

19. Processus xiphoideus is the "pomegranate."

20. These tunics are the vagina musculi recti abdominis.

21. Linea alba.

22. The guidez vein is the jugular vein.

23. Greater omentum.

24. Berengario apparently carried out operative procedures, as is indicated also by other evidence.

25. Hernia inguinalis.

26. Mucous secretion.

27. This is a true use of the word "villi"; as previously employed it refers to fibrous portions of muscles and tendons and has been translated as "fibers."

28. "Slender" refers to the small intestine.

29. vv. intestinales.

30. Ascends is a doubtful description.

31. Between the twelfth thoracic and the first lumbar vertebrae.

32. a. gastrica brevis; a. lienalis.

33. Renal vein.

34. Inferior vena cava.

35. Hepatic arteries.

36. This embryological structure is rather uncertain as an adult structure.

37. Falciform ligament; coronary hepatic ligament.

38. It is difficult to understand exactly what the author had in mind.

39. v. gastro-epiploica dextra.

40. v. mesenterica inferior.

41. v. mesenterica superior.

42. vv. colicae dextrae.
43. vv. intestinales.
44. a. sacralis media.
45. a. pudenda interna.
46. a. circumflexa ilium profunda.
47. a. haemorrhoidalis media et superior.
48. a. uterina.
49. a. obturatoria, ramus pubicus.
50. v. renalis; a. renalis.
51. Pelvis, or calyx, of the kidney.
52. Minor calyces.
53. a. spermatica interna; v. spermatica interna.
54. Many nerves from the plexus vesicalis are indicated here.
55. Prostate gland with the urethral sphincter.
56. This is possibly m. bulbo cavernosus.
57. Tenia coli.
58. There are four muscles: m. sphincter ani externus; m. levator ani; m. rectococ-cygeus; and m. sacrococcygeus anterior.
59. vv. haemorrhoidales, superiores et inferiores; v. hypogastrica.
60. Fimbria.

II. CONCERNING THE ANATOMY OF THE MIDDLE CAVITY

1. Collar bone.
2. Sternum.
3. a. mammaria interna, ramus perforans; a. axillaris, rami pectorales; v. mam-maria, ramus perforans; v. epigastrica inferior and branches of v. subclavica; vv. epigastricae superiores.
4. These foramina are the ducti lactiferi.
5. The following muscles move the chest voluntarily: subclavius; serratus an-terior; serratus posterior-superior; serratus posterior-inferior; iliocostales lum-borum et dorsi; transversus thoracis.
6. This muscle is either the m. subclavius, which does not attach to the scapula, or the m. serratus anterior, upper portion, which does attach to the scapula.
7. m. serratus anterior?
8. m. sternocleidomastoideus; serratus anterior?
9. m. rhomboideus minor et major.
10. m. serratus posterior superior.
11. The m. transversus thoracis above this pair equals m. subcostalis.
12. mm. intercostales interni et externi.

13. m. transversus thoracis et m. subcostalis.

14. Manubrium sterni; corpus sterni; processus xiphoideus.

15. Parietal peritoneum.

16. Capsule of the heart, or pericardium.

17. The natural are the visceral and the vital are the thoracic members or organs.

18. vv. and a. phrenicae interiores.

19. The two nerves which issue from the nape are the phrenic autonomic; the one from the brain is the vagus.

20. This statement probably refers to the sinus pericardialis obliquus.

21. Ostium arteriosum and ostium venosum ventriculi sinistri.

22. Ligaments, muscles, chordae tendineae, and papillary muscles.

23. Cuspis posterior valvulae tricuspidalis (right atrium).

24. The little skins are the valvulae semilunares or aa. pulmonales.

25. Unlike Vesalius, Berengario places these with the heart and not with the venous complex.

26. This vein is the sinus coronarius into which the v. cordis magna and v. cordis media empty.

27. These two pulsating veins are the a. coronaria dextra and a. coronaria sinistra.

28. Even Vesalius did not advance beyond this view of the triple sinus, that is, right and left halves of the heart with a sinus in the middle.

29. Septum musculare ventriculorum.

30. These little foramina proceed from Galenic teaching; Vesalius in the *Fabrica* denies their existence, but in the *Epitome* he acknowledges them.

31. Not until Harvey were these supposed openings proven not to exist.

32. Inferior and superior vena cava.

33. It is hard to grasp Berengario's conception of the venous drainage of the heart.

34. The foramina do not exist, and the diaphragm is the interventricular septum.

35. a. pulmonalis.

36. This amounts to a positive statement of the non-existence of foramina.

37. a. pulmonalis.

38. Valvulae semilunares.

39. These are the aorta and the pulmonary vein.

40. The tunica media is the "inner tunic."

41. Aorta.

42. Recurrent laryngeal.

43. Is this capillary circulation in the lung?

44. Semilunar valves of the aorta.

45. Pulmonary vein.

46. Bicuspid valve.

47. Is not this and the description above a very clear picture of the circulation of the blood? It would at least merit close attention as one of the best statements of the facts before the time of Harvey.
48. Vesalius did not recognize the three lobes on the right as Berengario does.
49. Bronchioli.
50. Trachea and two bronchi.
51. Pulmonary artery and vein.
52. A very simple expression of the function of the lungs.
53. This seems an excellent analogy.
54. Capillary net.
55. Visceral pleura.
56. Trachea and bronchi.
57. Right innominate and superior vena cava.
58. Aortic arch and left common carotid artery.
59. Pulmonary artery.
60. Pulmonary vein.
61. The change in content no doubt indicates a change in color.
62. Alveolar and capillary contact.
63. Cervical spinal cord.
64. Jugulars.
65. Vagus.
66. Nervi recurrentes.
67. m. sternocleidomastoideus.
68. Thyroid glands.
69. Carotid arteries.
70. Vagus nerve.
71. Recurrent laryngeal.
72. Inferior vena cava.
73. Sinus coronarius and its branches, vv. cordis magna et media.
74. Vena cava superior.
75. Right and left innominate veins continuing into the subclavians.
76. Carotids or jugular veins.
77. Tributaries to the jugular veins.
78. a. thoraco-acromialis.
79. a. transversa scapulae.
80. a. cervicalis profunda.
81. a. vertebralis.
82. a. axilla.
83. a. thoracalis suprema.

84. Rami pectorales.

85. a. mammaria interna.

86. a. mammaria interna.

87. a. thoracalis lateralis.

88. a. axillaris.

89. Probably v. transversa scapularis.

90. vv. faciales communes.

91. v. lingualis.

92. vv. thyreoideae superiores.

93. vv. auriculares anteriores.

94. Emissaria mastoidea; emissaria occipitalis.

95. Transverse sinus.

96. Emissaria parietalis.

97. This is an excellent description of all the converging veins which enter the transverse sinus drained by the internal jugular.

98. a. lingualis.

99. a. maxillaris interna; a. maxillaris externa.

100. a. temporalis superficialis.

101. a. occipitalis.

102. Medulla spinalis.

103. It is difficult to discover what the author meant by "light milky blood."

104. Internal carotid artery.

105. Cavernous sinus and its branches.

106. n. vagi.

107. Recurrent laryngeal nerve.

108. Here as well as in the works of Galen, Mundinus, and Vesalius the vagus is part of the sixth nerve complex which included the ninth, tenth, and eleventh pairs of cranial nerves.

109. n. vagi, ramus cardiacus superior.

110. n. vagi, rami gastrici; n. phrenicus.

111. n. vagi, rami lineales.

112. n. vagi, rami renales.

113. Recurrent laryngeal.

114. n. laryngei superiores.

115. The recurrent nerve does not close the epiglottis.

116. The nerves on the right go around the inferior surface of the a. subclavia.

117. The nerves on the left go around the aortic arch.

118. This is a most unusual observation.

119. These remarks are taken from Galen; see the historical note, p. 112.

120. m. frontalis.

121. Frontal bone.

122. Processus zygomaticus.

123. a. temporalis superficialis; vv. temporales superficiales.

124. Upper portion of the regio nasalis.

125. m. zygomaticus.

126. m. orbicularis oris.

127. These muscles are m. orbicularis oris; m. menti (doubtful); m. buccinator; m. zygomaticus; m. triangularis; m. nasalis; m. quadratus labii inferioris; m. caninus; m. incisivus labii superioris. There are more than six in all.

128. m. zygomaticus.

129. m. triangularis.

130. m. triangularis and m. buccinator.

131. n. cutaneus colli and n. auricularis magnus; both incorrect.

132. n. facialis; correct.

133. Dens incisivus, medialis et lateralis.

134. Dens caninus.

135. Dentes premolares.

136. Alveoli dentales.

137. Alveolares, superior et inferior.

138. Processus palatinus, os maxillare.

139. n. palatinus anterior, but not for the face.

140. This member is found in all primates.

141. aa. palatinae major et minor; vv. palatinae major et minor.

142. m. uvulae; m. levator veli palatini; m. tensor veli palatini.

143. n. lingualis, of touch; n. facialis, chorda tympani, of taste; n. glossopharyngeus; n. hypoglossus, of movement.

144. a. lingualis and v. lingualis.

145. How the author arrived at this deduction is difficult to discover.

146. These muscles are the intrinsic m. longitudinalis inferior et superior, with m. verticalis and m. transversus; extrinsic m. styloglossus; m. genoglossus; m. hypoglossus; m. glossopharyngeus; m. glossopalatenus. These number nine.

147. m. styloglossus.

148. It is possible that Berengario is referring to both the stylohyoideus and the stylopharyngeus.

149. The styloid process.

150. Hyoid bone.

151. The epiglottis is not fastened to the hyoid bone.

152. m. hypoglossus.

153. m. thyreohyoideus.

154. m. omohyoideus.

155. m. sternohyoideus.

156. m. digastricus; m. geniohyoideus; m. mylohyoideus.

157. m. digastricus to m. hypoglossus.

158. m. geniohyoideus.

159. m. stylohyoideus.

160. a. lingualis; v. lingualis.

161. Ductus submaxillaris.

162. Submaxillary gland and frenulum linguae.

163. Mucous membrane.

164. Mucous glands.

165. Arcus glossopalatinus, arcus pharyngopalatinus, and plica triangularis.

166. Fossa supratonsillaris.

167. m. temporalis; m. masseter.

168. nn. temporales profundi.

169. The fourth pair is certainly incorrect.

170. This is inaccurate.

171. m. masseter.

172. The author is mistaken both as to action and position of these muscles.

173. Berengario's idea of the pterygoids is incorrect as to the position; the function of the buccinator is here confused with mastication.

174. Trachea.

175. These cartilages are the thyroid, cricoid, arytenoid, and corniculata.

176. Thyroid cartilage.

177. Cricoid cartilage.

178. Cornu inferius.

179. Arytenoid cartilage.

180. m. cricothyroidei, pars recta, pars obliqua; m. cricoarytenoideus, lateralis et posterior.

181. m. arytenoepiglotticus; m. arytenoideus obliquus; m. thyreoepiglotticus; m. arytenoideus transversus.

182. Esophagus.

183. n. vagus.

184. Recurrent laryngeal.

III. CONCERNING THE UPPERMOST BODY CAVITY

1. Venous plexuses.

2. The lateral, third and fourth.

3. Choroid plexus.

4. Vermis of the cerebellum.

5. Periosteum.

6. Probably sutures, which Berengario calls both "commissures" and "pores."

7. The traditional belief in vapors, etc., was strong.

8. Frontal sinus.

9. Temporal bone.

10. The insertion of the m. sternocleidomastoideus.

11. The mastoid process and the styloid process.

12. Occipital and sphenoid bones.

13. Sutura lambdoidea.

14. Sutura sagittalis.

15. Sutura squamosa.

16. Sutura parietomastoidea or sphenoparietalis.

17. Superior sagittal suture.

18. Torcular Herophili.

19. Cerebral veins.

20. The "worms" are plexus chorioideus ventriculi lateralis.

21. Gyri et sulci.

22. Cerebrum.

23. Divided by the falx cerebri.

24. Inferior horn, lateral ventricle.

25. Plexus chorioideus ventriculi lateralis.

26. Could he mean the head of the caudate nucleus?

27. Foramen of Monro.

28. Pituitary gland.

29. Third ventricle.

30. Lamina cribrosa of the ethmoid bone.

31. The aqueduct of Sylvius, reaching to the fourth ventricle, which descends toward the medulla spinalis.

32. Plexus chorioideus of the fourth ventricle.

33. Pineal gland.

34. Following his mentor Mundinus, Berengario, like Galen and Vesalius, gives seven as the number of the cranial nerves.

35. This idea comes to Berengario from the Alexandrian school of medicine through Galen and Mundinus.

36. Olfactory bulbs.

37. Lamina cribosa of the ethmoid bone.

38. Frontal sinuses.

39. Optic nerves, first pair.

40. Optic chiasma.
41. Oculomotor nerves, second pair.
42. The trochlear is not mentioned.
43. The trigeminal is united with the sixth pair which according to **Berengario** is the vagus and recurrent nerves, third pair.
44. Ophthalmic and maxillary branches.
45. Trigeminal, mandicular branch, fourth pair.
46. Facial and auditory nerves, fifth pair.
47. Glossopharyngeal, vagus and spinal accessors, sixth pair.
48. Hypoglossal, seventh pair.
49. See the table on p. 211.
50. Internal carotids.
51. The central branches of the circle of Willis: this is Berengario's unseen rete mirabile.
52. No doubt these are the middle cerebral arteries.
53. Anterior choroidal arteries.
54. Pituitary gland.
55. m. quadrati labii superioris.
56. The cartilages are: (*a*) cartilago septi nasi; (*b*) cartilago alaris major and crus laterale and crus mediale; (*c*) cartilago nasi lateralis.
57. Ossa nasalia, perforated with the foramen nasale.
58. Lamina cribrosa, ossa ethmoidalia.
59. Mammillary carunculae refers to a collection of gray matter which forms part of, or gives rise to, the olfactory nerve—the tuberculum olfactorium.
60. Lamina cribrosa of the ethmoid bone.
61. Like a cartilage but not true cartilage.
62. Ungula is equivalent to "hoof," sebel to sebacious, and verrucae to warts.
63. Orbicularis oculi, pars orbitalis, pars palpebralis, pars lacrimalis; these muscles are not clearly described.
64. m. corrugator: a large cautery here naturally would not affect the movement of the eyes, because this muscle is not connected with the lids.
65. The eyelids belong to the muscles of facial expression. Berengario was fully aware of common enervation of the muscles of facial expression, but he was confused as to the origin of the seventh nerve.
66. Papilla lacrimalis with puncta lacrimalis.
67. The proper muscles of the eyes: mm. recti inferior, superior, lateralis, and medialis; m. obliquus superior and inferior. The seventh, not ocular, is the m. levator palpebrae superioris.
68. Tunic I, conjunctiva.
69. Tunic II, cornea.

COMPARATIVE TABLE OF CRANIAL NERVES

	Modern Usage	Galen	Mundinus	Berengario	Vesalius
I.	Olfactory.......	Not regarded as separate nerves	Not regarded as separate nerves	Not regarded as separate nerves	Not regarded as separate nerves
II.	Optic...........	"The soft nerves of the eyes"	First pair	First pair	First pair
III.	Oculomotor.....	"The nerves moving both eyes"	Second pair	Second pair	Second pair
IV.	Trochlear.......	Not described	Not mentioned	Probably included with "second pair"	Included with "second pair"
V.	Trigeminal......	{"Third pair of nerves"	Third pair	Third pair, which has two roots united with fourth and sixth pairs	Third pair, which has two roots
		"Fourth pair of nerves"	Fourth pair	Fourth pair	Fourth pair
VI.	Abducens.......	United with optic	Not mentioned	Not mentioned	Included with second pair
VII.	Facial ⎫.......	"Fifth pair of nerves"	Fifth pair	Fifth pair	Fifth pair
VIII.	Auditory ⎰				
IX.	Glossopha- ⎫ ryngeal			Sixth pair mixed with the third	Sixth pair; also includes sympathetic trunk with this cranial nerve
X.	Vagus ⎬.....	"Sixth pair of nerves"	Sixth pair		
XI.	Spinal ac- ⎭ cessory				
XII.	Hypoglossal.....	"Seventh pair of nerves"	Seventh pair	Seventh pair	Seventh pair

70. Tunic III, the sclera attached to the dura mater. It is unusual that Berengario should have understood this true connection.

71. Tunic IV, the uvea (coronoidea), choroid coat.

72. Secundina? Pigmented epithelion?

73. Retina, pars ciliaris and pars optica.

74. Crystalline lens.

75. Auditory canal.

76. Cavum tympani.

77. See the table on p. 211.

78. Malleus, incus.

79. Bilateral maxillae.

80. The ancient physicians called any canal or conduit a colatorium, and embotum in this case is embotum cerebri, infundibulum of the brain.

81. Foramen magnum and spinal cord, termed nape by Berengario.

IV. CONCERNING THE ANATOMY OF THE EXTREMITIES

1. Nothos, meaning dorsum, vertebral column, is a misspelling of notos. Notiaeos and nuca, the nape, correspond to the medulla spinalis.

2. Occipital condyles.

3. Facies articularis superior.

4. The atlanto-occipital ligament as well as the articular capsule.

5. The piroidea is the dens.

6. Thoracic vertebrae.

7. Cauda equina.

8. Eight cervical, twelve thoracic, five lumbar, five sacral, one coccygeal, and the filum terminale.

9. These include seven pairs of cranial nerves, thirty-one pairs of spinal nerves, the filum terminale, and the olfactory nerves, for a total of seventy-nine.

10. Eight pairs if the olfactory nerves are included.

11. The distribution should be sacral, five, and coccygeal, one.

12. By "glandulous flesh" Berengario probably means the lymph nodes.

13. The adiutorium is the humerus.

14. v. mediana cubiti.

15. vv. metacarpeae dorsales.

16. An excellent statement of anatomical variation.

17. The hand is the upper extremity in this case.

18. Scapula.

19. Cavitas glenoidalis.

20. Acromion.

21. Processus coracoideus.
22. The epicondyles medialis et lateralis are the eminences.
23. Fossa olecrani et trochlea humeri.
24. Radius; ulna.
25. Ossa pisiforme, triquetrum, hamatum, lunatum, capitatum; naviculare manus; multangulum minus et maius.
26. The row.
27. Tendons of the m. extensor digitorum communis.
28. v. saphena parva.
29. Inguinal lymph glands and veins.
30. v. femoralis.
31. Pubes.
32. Femur.
33. Haunch.
34. Ligamentum teres.
35. Tibia and fibula.
36. Patella.
37. Talus.
38. Os calcaneum.
39. Ossa cuboideum, cuneiforme I, II, III.
40. Ossa metatarsalia.
41. m. extensor hallucis longus et m. extensor digitorum longus.
42. m. flexor digitorum longus.

BIBLIOGRAPHY

BIBLIOGRAPHY

THE BIBLIOGRAPHY of Berengario da Carpi has not yet been exhaustively explored. Vittorio Putti has brought together the chief items on the subject without making a comprehensive search for extant copies of the various editions; see pages 131–62 of his book. It is my purpose here only to present a list of Berengario's works and of books used in making this translation, with an asterisk before each item which deals in whole or in part with Berengario. It will quickly be seen how little has been written about him. I believe that nothing of importance from modern times has escaped me; my search has been based upon the *Index Medicus,* the *Quarterly Cumulative Index,* and the *Index Catalogue of the Library of the Surgeon-General's Office,* U.S. Army; on the files of various journals of the history of medicine; on the bibliographies in *Isis* and other similar sources. It may be noted here that the Medical History Library at Yale University has a copy of all the works of Berengario except the *Commentary.* These copies can now be added to the number of copies listed as extant by Putti, i.e., the *Isagogae* of 1522, 1523, 1530, and the *De fractura cranei* of 1518, 1535, 1626, 1715.

THE WORKS OF BERENGARIO DA CARPI

1514

Anothomia Mundini noiuter [sic] *impressa ac per Carpum castigata.* Impressa per Iustinianum Ruberie, Bologna. Quarto, 26 folios, 4 copies extant. Other editions: Venice, 1529, 4 copies; 1530?, 3 copies; 1538, 2 copies.

1518

Tractatus de Fractura Calue siue Cranei a Carpo editus. Impressum per Hieronymum de Benedictis (Benedetti), Bologna. Quarto, 105 folios, 8 copies extant. Other editions: Bologna, 15——, 1 copy; Venice, 1535, 14 copies; Leiden, 1629, 7 copies; Leiden, 1651, 1 copy; Leiden, 1715, 3 copies; Leiden, 1728, 1 copy. The last three are reprints of the 1629 edition.

1521

Carpi Commentaria cum amplissimis additionibus super anatomia Mundini una cum textu eiusdem in pristinum et verum nitorem redacto. Impressum per Hieronymum de Benedictis, Bologna. Quarto, 528a folios, 8 copies extant.

1521

Ulrichi de Hutten eq. de guaiaci medicina et morbo Gallico liber unus. (Fol. 39b, "procurante Carpo.") Impressum per Hieronymum de Benedictis, Bologna. Quarto, 39 folios, 2 copies extant.

1522

Habes in hoc volumine candide lector magni Galeni Pergamensis medicorum principis libros tres de crisi. i. de iudicationibus interprete Laurentiano Medico Florentino. (Fols. 2–3a, "excellentissimo amplissimoque artium et medicinae doctori ac preceptori suo Iacobo Carpo, Ochoa goncalez de Butron cantaber salutem.") In aedibus Hieronymi de Benedictis, Bologna. Quarto, 57 folios, 1 copy extant.

1522

Isagoge Breues perlucide ac uberrime in Anatomiam humani corporis a communi Medicorum Academia usitatam a Carpo in Almo Bononiensi Gymnasio Ordinariam Chirurgie publice Docente ad suorum Scholasticorum preces in lucem date. Impressum per Benedictum Hectoris (Faelli), Bologna. Quarto, 72 folios, 5 copies extant. Other editions: Bologna, 1523, folios 80a, 9 copies; Strassburg, 1530, folios 133, octavo, 4 copies; Bologna, 1535, folios 63, quarto, 13 copies.

1529

Galeni Pergameni Libri Anatomici, quorum indicem uersa pagina indicabit. De motu musculorum liber primus, Nicolao Leoniceno vicentino interprete. Anatomicarum aggressionum, interprete Demetrio Chalcondylo. De arteriarum et venarum dissectione, interprete Antonio Fortolo Ioseriensi. De hirudinibus, revulsione etc., interprete Ferdinando Balamio Siculo. In aedibus Ioannis Baptistae Phaelli, Bologna. Quarto, folios 24 numbered, 128 unnumbered, 1 copy extant.

1660

Microcosmographia [in Greek]: *or, a Description of the Little World or Body of Man. Being a brief and practical Anatomy of the Body of Man; not only shewing a Methodical description of the parts, but also the manner of Anatomizing from part to part; the like of which hath not been set forth in the English Tongue; Adorned with many plain demonstrative figures. Which was long since composed in Latine, by that famous Jacobus Berengario of Carpus, Doctor of Arts and Physick, and Reader of Chirurgery in the University of Bononia; and now done into English, and published for Publick use by Henry Jackson Chirurgeon. By whom is also added a fit Etymon to the Names of the parts in their proper place.* Printed by R. I. for Livewell Chapman, at the sign of the Crown in Popes-head Alley, London.

1664

Microcosmographia [in Greek]: *or, a description of the body of man. Being a Practical Anatomy shewing the Manner of Anatomizing from Part to Part; The like hath not been set forth in the English Tongue. Adorned with many demonstrative Figures. Long since Composed in Latine, by that famous J. Berengarius of Carpus, Dr. of A. and P. Reader of Chirurgery in the University of Bononia. Done into English by H. Jackson Chirurgeon. By whom is also added a fit Etymon to the Names of the Parts, in their proper place.* Printed for Livewell Chapman, at his shop in Exchange Alley in Corn Hill, London. This issue is the same as that of 1660, as shown by Larkey and Tum Suden, except for the change in address of the printer and the shorter title. I know of 4 copies of the 1660 edition of this translation, one in practically perfect condition, even with some leaves uncut, in the Medical Historical Library of the University of Kansas. Of the 1664 issue there are at least 3 copies extant; no doubt more than these copies could be found in the world today.

OTHER BOOKS AND ARTICLES

*"The Anatomical Library of Dr. Richard Mead (1673–1754)," *Journal of the History of Medicine,* II (1947), 99. Dr. Mead owned a 1530 and a 1535 *Isagogae breves.*

ARTELT, WALTER. *Einführung in die Medizinhistorik.* Stuttgart, 1949.

*BARBOSA, SUEIRO, M. B. "Jacó Berengario da Carpi: Notas sóbre a sua vida e obra," *Arquivo de anatomia e antropologia* (Lisbon), XIII (1929–30), 387–95.

*BROWN, ALFRED JEROME. "Jacob Berengarius of Carpi, concerning Fracture of the Skull," in *Old Masterpieces of Surgery* (Chicago, 1928), pp. 67–71.

BROWNE, E. G. *Arabian Medicine.* Cambridge University Press, 1921.

*CASTIGLIONI, ARTURO. *A History of Medicine.* 2d ed. New York, 1947.

CAVERNI, RAFFAELE. *Storia del metodo sperimentale in Italia.* Florence, 1893.

CHOULANT, L. *History and Bibliography of Anatomic Illustration.* Translated with Preface by M. FRANK. Chicago, 1920.

*CLARK, E. W. LE GROS. "Berengario da Carpi," *St. Thomas's Hospital Gazette* (London), XXXII (1929–30), 110–21.

CORNER, GEORGE W. *Anatomical Texts of the Earlier Middle Ages,* etc. Carnegie Institution of Washington, 1927.

CROMBIE, A. C. *From Augustine to Galileo.* London, 1952.

*DANA, CHARLES L. "Where Apollo Strikes the Lyre: A Study of the Canticles of the Old Anatomists," *Proceedings of the Charaka Club* (New York), III (1910), 43–62.

DUNGLISON, ROBLEY. *A Dictionary of Medical Science.* Rev. ed. Philadelphia, 1874.

FAVARO, G. J. *Berengario nella storia dell'anatomia.* Modena, 1931.

*FISCHER, KARL. "Die Nomina anatomica in der 'Isagogae' des Berengario da Carpi: Ein Beitrag zur anatomischen Nomenklatur vor Vesal." Leipzig medical dissertation, 1943. (Unavailable to me.)

FONAHN, ADOLF. "Arabic and Latin Anatomical Terminology, Chiefly from the Middle Ages," *Videnskapsselskapets Skrifter* (Oslo: Norwegian Academy of Sciences), II, *Hist. filos. Klasse,* No. 7 (1922), pp. 1–174.

GALEN. *Opera omnia.* 7 vols. in 4. Venice: Giunta, 1625.

*GELATI, A. "Jacopo Berengario da Carpi," *Memorie storiche sulla città di Carpi* (Carpi), Vol. II (1879–80).

*GRIMELLI, G. *Sopra il metodo antisifilitico di Jacopo Berengario da Carpi.* Modena: Soliani, 1884.

HYRTL, JOSEPH. *Das Arabische und Hebraische in der Anatomia.* Vienna, 1879.

HYRTL, JOSEPH. *Onomatologia anatomica: Geschichte und Kritik der anatomischen Sprache der Gegenwart,* etc. Vienna, 1880.

*JOURDAN, A. J. L. "Berengario (Jacques)" in *Dictionaire* [sic] *des sciences médicales, Biographie médicale* (Paris: Panckoucke, 1820), II, 155–58.

KELLETT, C. E., "A Note on Rosso and the Illustrations to Charles Estienne's *De dissectione," Journal of the History of Medicine and Allied Sciences,* XII [1957], 325–36.

——. *Two Anatomies: An Occasional Lecture on the "De dissectione" of Charles Estienne Given to the University of Durham Dental Students on the 8th May, 1958.*

*LARKEY, SANFORD V., and TUM SUDEN, LINDA. "Jackson's English Translation of Berengarius of Carpi's *Isagogae breves,* 1660 and 1664," *Isis,* XXI (1934), 57–70.

*MAJOR, RALPH H. *A History of Medicine.* 2 vols. Springfield, Ill.: Charles C Thomas, 1954.

*MARTINOTTI, G. "L'insegnamento dell'anatomia in Bologna prima del secolo XIX," *Studi e Memorie per la storia dell'Università di Bologna* (Bologna, 1911).

*——. "Il Testamento di Maestro Jacobo Barigazzi o Berengario da Carpi," *Rivista di storia delle scienze mediche e naturali* (Florence, 1923), Vol. XIV, Nos. 3–4.

*MEDICI, M. *Comp. storia della scuola anatomica di Bologna.* Bologna, 1857.

**Memorie storiche e documenti sulla città e sull'antico principato di Carpi* (Carpi), Vol. VII (1894–95).

*MONTEIRO, H. "Leonardo da Vinci, Berengario da Carpi, and Andreas Vesalius, Three Celebrated Anatomists of the Italian Renaissance," *J. med. Pôrto* (1943), Nos. 62–63, pp. 1–20. *In* Arquivo de trabalhos da Faculdade de medicina do Pôrto, Biblioteca da Faculdade de medicina do Pôrto, Portugal.

*PARDAL, R. "Pre-Vesalian Renaissance Anatomy," *Revista de la Asociación médica argentina* (Buenos Aires), LIX (1945), 586–89.

*PAZZINI, ADALBERTO. *Bibliografia di storia della medicina italiana.* Milan, 1939.

*——. *Storia della medicina.* Vol. I. Milan, 1947.

*PILCHER, LEWIS STEPHEN. "Jacobus Berengarius Carpensis and His Commentaries on Mundinus," *Medical Library and Historical Journal* (Brooklyn, N.Y.), I (1903), 1–8.

POLLUX, JULIUS. *Onomasticon,* ed. E. BETHE. ("Lexicographi Graeci," Vol. IX, fasc. 1–3.) Leipzig, 1900–1937. See also W. Dindorf's ed., 1824.

*PUTTI, VITTORIO. *Berengario da Carpi: Saggio biografico e bibliografico seguito dalla traduzione del "De fractura calvae sive cranei."* Bologna: L. Cappelli, 1937.

*"Nel quarto centenario della morte di Jacopo Berengario da Carpi," *Memorie accad. sci. inst. Bologna,* VIII (1931), 3–11.

*RENZI, SALVATORE DE. *Storia della medicina italiana.* Vols. I–V. Naples, 1845–48.

*ROTH, MORITZ. *Andreas Vesalius Bruxellensis.* Berlin, 1892.

*RUSSELL, K. F. "Jacopo Berengario da Carpi," *Australian and New Zealand Journal of Surgery,* XXIII (1953), 70–72.

BIBLIOGRAPHY

SINGER, CHARLES. *The "Fasciculo di Medicina," Venice, 1493: A Translation of the "Anathomia" of Mondino da Luzzi. (Monumenta Medica.* Vol. II.) Milan: R. LIER, 1924.

*———. *The Evolution of Anatomy.* London, 1925.

——— (ed.). *Studies in the History and Method of Science.* 2 vols. Oxford: Oxford University Press, 1917–21.

*STEUDEL, J. "Der vorvesalische Beitrag zur anatomischen Nomenklatur," *Sudhoffs Archiv für Geschichte der Medizin und der Naturwissenschaftern,* XXXVI (1943), 1–42.

*THORNDIKE, LYNN. "Anatomy from Carpi to Vesalius," *A History of Magic and Experimental Science* (New York: Columbia University Press, 1941), Vol. V, chap. xxiii.

*TIRABOSCHI, GIROLAMO. *Biblioteca Modenese,* Vol. VI.

*VEDRANI, A. "Berengario da Carpi," *Illust. med. ital.,* IV (1922), 108–11.

VESALIUS. *Epitome.* Translated by L. R. LIND, with anatomical notes by C. W. ASLING. New York: Macmillan Co., 1949.

INDEX
TO ANATOMICAL TERMS

INDEX

TO ANATOMICAL TERMS

Date Due

DEC 1 2 '65	Jan 11 66				
Dec 14/65	JAN 1 8 '66				
DEC 1 4 '65					
DEC 1 5 '65					
DEC 1 7 '65					
Dec 18/65 DEC 2 0 '65					
JAN 7 '66					
JAN 1 0 '66					